921 '86
Clark

Clark
Lady with a spear.

Date Due

NOV 2 1967	MAR 2 9 1978		AP 13 01
MAR 1 1068		MR '84	NR 4 05
MAR 1 9 1968		MAR 31 85	SO. 53 UN
APR 1 5 1968	MY 3 '91	CKEN	MY 20 '05 MY 20 05
MAY 1 5 1968	MK 31 '90	JAN 7 '98	MY 18 07 JY 03 07
Small MAR 19 '91		98. 98 NO 20 '98	
OCT 1 0 1969		CKEN	
LG	APR 8 '93	MR 14 '98	
MAY 7 76	MR 18 '94 MX 11	OC 30 '98	
MAY 25 1972	MR 1 '94	FE 4	
		MAR 20	

LADY with a SPEAR

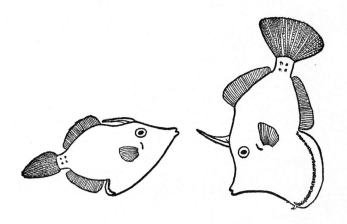

Eugenie Clark

LADY with a SPEAR

Harper & Row · Publishers · New York · Evanston · London

To Yumico
and Masatomo Nobu

Contents

Illustrations

The illustrations, grouped in a separate section, will be found following page 84.

Dr. Carl L. Hubbs of the Scripps Institute

The author on the *E. W. Scripps*

The author with Clarence and Pedro

A pair of courting guppies

Siakong, a great spearfisherman

Siakong, Niraibui, and an old fisherman

Native Sonsorol spearfisherman holding triggerfish

An old woman weaving a basket on Merir Island

Ueg, King of Ulithi, in his royal wagon

The author among the high chiefs of Fais

A drying throw net

The author with a throw net

The author demonstrating the method for opening a throw net

The author attempting to release a throw net

Acknowledgments

This past year it has been great fun reminiscing, for the purposes of this book, about my work and about experiences which, and people who, directly or indirectly have made the pursuit of fish knowledge a delightful way of life for me. I owe special thanks to those who have helped me assemble these reminiscences in this form.

I doubt that I would have started without the encouragement of Elizabeth Lawrence and Marie F. Rodell. Their interest and helpful suggestions initiated and nourished the writing of this book.

Writing about my experiences informally, for publication, began several years ago when Edward M. Weyer, Jr., the Editor of *Natural History Magazine* helped me struggle through my first "popular" article. Dr. Weyer has kindly given permission to incorporate in this book a series of articles published in his magazine. For the earliest encouragement in writing, however, I would like to express my thanks to Professor Frederika Beatty who made a freshman course in composition as fascinating for me as one in ichthyology. I find the seeds for the first chapter of this book in compositions I wrote during Professor Beatty's course.

I am very grateful for two Fellowships in writing given to me in 1952. The Eugene Saxton Memorial Fellowship enabled me to have financial independence for the writing of this book. The Breadloaf Writer's Fellowship enabled me to attend their Conference where samples of my writing were read and criticized by professional writers and critics. I wish particularly to express my gratitude to Fletcher Pratt and John Fischer for their invaluable criticisms.

Mrs. Hedwig Englert generously offered to proofread and type the final draft of this manuscript—a record-breaking job that she finished the day before she delivered a baby.

And a final word of thanks to my husband who never blinked an eye the many evenings he came home late, tired, and hungry and found me at the typewriter with supper not even started.

The picture of me demonstrating the use of a throw net in the museum is by courtesy of Mr. Thane Bierwert. The picture of a Mako shark is reprinted by permission of the Marine Biological Station, Ghardaqa. I am also grateful to the Reverend William Walter, S. J., for permission to use the photograph of me releasing the throw net from the top of a rock.

LADY with a SPEAR

Getting Acquainted with Fish

I took several fast deep breaths, adjusted my face mask, checked the safety lock on my speargun, and dived back down again into the Red Sea. The ledge under which the orange and brown striped scorpion fish was hiding was about ten feet down. This was going to be an easy catch. I reached the ledge and, being careful not to touch the poisonous corals growing on it, got a grip on the ledge to hold myself down. Slowly I aimed my speargun at a creature that looked like a brilliant flower with delicate attenuated petals. It barely moved at my approach, depending on the venomous spines hiding in those "petals" for its protection. . . .

That may read like science fiction, or a dream. It isn't fiction, but it is a dream—a dream come true. I had dreamed it first one autumn morning in New York, when I was nine years old.

It was a Saturday and so there was no school. My mother

took me downtown with her on her way to work and deposited
me in a large building at Battery Park. "Amuse yourself until
I'm through," she said. "Then we'll go have lunch."

So casually, so by chance, I entered the world of water. For
this was the Old Aquarium that used to stand at the tip of Man-
hattan. All about me were glass tanks with moving creatures in
them. At the back was a tank larger than the others, and the
water in it was less clear, more mysterious. It was pale green
and, a few feet from the glass wall that I looked through, it
grew misty, as if there were no farther wall and the water just
went on and on. Leaning over the brass railing, I brought my
face as close as possible to the glass and pretended I was walking on the bottom of the sea.

I went to the Aquarium again the next Saturday. And the
next. And all the Saturdays that followed. I never tired of watching the fish—from the streamlined, fast-swimming ones gliding
back and forth in their long tanks like caged tigers, with barely
a perceptible movement to explain their swift motion, to the
sluggish, bottom-creeping forms that seemed to exert enormous
effort through their whole bodies to inch along.

I had always liked the water, whether I was jumping and
tumbling in the rough, salty breakers off Long Island, or swimming in the smooth fresh water of a pool. In spite of salt or
chlorine, I always kept my eyes open when my head was underwater, trying to make out something through the green blur—
the pebbly bottom of the beach, the tiling or drain at the bottom
of the pool, or just my own feet.

My mother began taking me to the beach before I was two

years old. She had once been a swimming teacher and liked the water almost more than I did. My whole family—that is to say, grandma, uncle, and mama—all loved the beach. And all of them were expert swimmers. My uncle did fancy diving. I'd call my friends over to watch him and talk loudly so everyone could hear: "There's my uncle. Watch him now, he's going to do a somersault."

But it was with a quieter and secret pleasure that I watched my mother. Her strokes were rhythmical and graceful, and she swam long distances effortlessly. When she came out of the water she would take off her bathing cap, and her jet black hair, which she usually wore pinned up in conservative Japanese fashion, fell down to her hips. She looked more Oriental then than in the pictures I'd seen of her in kimonos when she was a young girl in Japan; she looked like a pearl diver of the Orient. When I overheard the admiring remarks that strangers made about her, I didn't claim her as I did my uncle; I just listened quietly, secure in the knowledge that soon she would call me over and everyone would know she was my mother.

One of the first things that intrigued me about mama swimming, was that she put chewing gum in her ears. I didn't know why she did it, but it looked like a chic thing to do. So the first time I was allowed to chew gum, I lost no time stuffing it into my ears—along with much of my hair. But I soon learned the technique as well as the reason for it. Gum can be molded to the exact shape of the ear opening, as a plug to keep the water out, and natural wax prevents it from sticking in the ear. I got a big kick out of the ritual of sitting on the beach with mama while we chewed gum and then plugged it into our ears before our first dip. It made me feel like a professional swimmer.

I wasn't much of a swimmer, however. I could manage to stay up or down if I wanted to, but my strokes, in spite of my family's coaching, were irregular and clumsy. I always enjoyed watching really good swimmers and those Saturdays at the Aquarium in Battery Park, I started watching the best of them —the fish.

I'd given little thought before to how a fish swims. As far as I'd considered, swimming was a co-ordinated movement of arms and legs. How did fish get along so well without these important appendages? I watched them a long time before realizing that even the appendages fish do have—their tails and other fins—are used mostly for turning and balancing and that it is their powerful body muscles that propel them through the water.

At lunchtime, mother came to the Aquarium to fetch me, and we would walk over to Fuji, a tiny Japanese restaurant on Greenwich Street. We often had Oriental dishes at home but some of the rarer ingredients had to be replaced by the closest substitute our local grocery carried. Nobusan, the proprietor of Fuji, took pride in the authenticity of his dishes. He went to great lengths to obtain dried or canned bamboo shoots, water chestnuts and seaweeds, as well as the best grade of soy sauce and rare spices and pickled products imported from the Orient. He knew the best shops and markets to buy fresh ginger, squid, octopi, and canned abalone. The latter he got in Chinatown— where he ate on his days off. For a restaurant that seated less than thirty people, Fuji had an extraordinary menu. Sukiyaki with beef, pork or chicken was made right at the table. Nobusan let his customers know whenever he was able to get a particularly good tuna—for *sashimi* or raw fish, especially the red flesh from a fresh tuna, is a treat for Japanese living in New York.

And so often, while we ate *sashimi* and dipped crisp dried seaweed into soy sauce and wrapped it around hot rice with our chopsticks, I would tell mama about the living fish I had watched at the Aquarium that morning. At the beginning of December, I started stressing a section of the balcony exhibits that displayed dozens of "home aquaria" with small tropical fish.

"Can you imagine, mama," I would say innocently, "people can have these beautiful fish right in their own homes and watch them all the time?" She kept on eating. She knew what my real question was.

One Saturday, instead of going to a movie after lunch, we went down to Nassau Street to pick out my Christmas present. I coaxed her into buying me a large fifteen-gallon aquarium. We had to get some gravel and a few large stones to give the bottom a "natural" look, a variety of aquatic plants including the emerald long-leaved Vallisnaria, and some coral-red snails. It was the most exciting spending spree either of us had ever known. We picked out a pair of veil-tailed guppies, black-speckled red platies, pale green swordtails, striped danios, iridescent pearl danios, "head-and-tail lights," a weird looking scavenger fish with "whiskers," and a pair of graceful angelfish. When I saw a clown fish I wanted, my mother informed me that we were way over what she had planned to spend for

Christmas. "Couldn't this count as my birthday present?" I persisted. "But that's not until May," she exclaimed. Then the red-banded clown swam into full view. "Well—" said my mother. I got the clown fish, too.

Before we left the shop, we had lost track of how many years' Christmas and birthday presents I had in advance. She had even bought me a big book full of colored pictures of aquarium fishes.

As the months passed, our small three-room apartment turned into a menagerie. My weekly allowance all went toward this hobby which fascinated both of us. Several times a week, mother would come home with little white cardboard packages, carefully held upright, and I knew she had spent her lunch hour in a pet shop again and had brought home some new addition to our fast-growing collection.

A friend from school brought me some salamanders he had collected and so we made a terrarium that was like a little corner on the floor of a woods. We acquired an intriguing horned "toad" and he lived in a glass cage we referred to as the "desert." Our alligator gave his aquarium the atmosphere of a jungle river. I would stare at him as he lay in the water, with only his eyes and snout above the surface, and he would seem to grow until he became a large, ferocious reptile. But then he would open his jaws wide and in place of the mighty roar of a giant alligator came a squeaky "oink"—and he shrank back again to baby size.

But it was the horned toad who played the single most important role—for he "saved" my soul.

He would eat only meal worms and they were hard to get.

One day I was introduced to a man who, I learned, had a large collection of fish and other animals. He invited me to see it. It was the most amazing menagerie I've ever seen outside of a zoo. Fish all over the house; one room devoted entirely to birds; and in various corners were cages of snakes, lizards, turtles, etc. Mr. Stephans was well known. Whenever anyone tired of his pet, or it got too sickly to be attractive, it was turned over to Mr. Stephans, who nursed it back to health and would free-board it indefinitely or until the owner wanted it back. If someone sent you a poor helpless little turtle with your name painted on its back, and you didn't know what to do with it, Mr. Stephans would take care of it.

If you don't believe that the rabbit's famed power of pro-liferating is overshadowed by the guppy, ask the man who started with a single pair and now has to pour his baby guppies down the drain, for lack of space to keep them. After a single mating with a male, the female guppy may have as many as nine broods totaling several hundred offspring—even though she be placed in isolation after this one mating. Only Mr. Stephans could always find a spare aquarium if you brought him your surplus.

His cellar contained the less attractive members of his menag-erie. "So you have trouble getting the proper food for your horned toad, do you? Well, just come and look at this." He led me over to a small chest and pulled out one of the drawers. It was half full of what appeared to be sawdust, on top of which a black beetle crawled. Mr. Stephans dug his fingers into what he explained was corn meal and came up with some fat wriggling worms that I recognized immediately as the meal worms my horned toad ate. There must have been hundreds in that drawer. Mr. Stephans explained that they were really the larval stages of the black beetle I had just seen.

During that first visit to Mr. Stephans' house, I was full of enthusiasm and kept praising his wonderful collection of pets. But he always passed the credit on to their Creator. I finally learned he was the pastor of a nearby chapel. "Why don't you come over and see our chapel this Sunday?" he asked.

I'd never been in a church. I was less than two when my American father died. I knew only my mother's side of the family. Grandma, of Japanese-Scotch mixture, was originally raised as a Christian in China, but she married a Japanese doctor who was a Shintoist, and her children developed leanings toward Buddhism. It was complicated and no one had ever bothered about my religious training. I always felt I enjoyed a certain freedom that my friends, who had to get up early on Sundays for church, didn't have. I didn't want to get involved in anything that might jeopardize this religious independence. While I mentally planned a polite refusal, Mr. Stephans added, "On the way back from church, I'll give you enough meal worms to last your horned toad until the next Sunday."

So I started going to church regularly. In addition to the meal worms, I sometimes got a bonus of a baby fish or two that had been born during the week in Mr. Stephans' menagerie. Eventually, I was baptized for a snake and confirmed for Ditmars' *Book of Reptiles*.

Through Mr. Stephans, I became the youngest member who had ever been accepted in the Queens County Aquarium Society and my fervor for collecting and studying fishes increased in geometric proportions. I began keeping a methodical record of my pets, their scientific names, the date I got each specimen, and what happened to it.

It was an exciting event when my pair of Siamese fighting fish started mating. It was in the evening after supper and mama and I watched together. The male had built a bubble nest at the surface of the water in one corner of the aquarium. Under this he wrapped his mate in his long flowing fins, squeezing her body till the eggs dropped out. Then he carefully picked the eggs up in his mouth and placed them in the nest. After a few days of anxious waiting, we spotted the wiggling tails of almost microscopic baby fish, hanging from the bottom of the nest. Soon over a hundred of them were swimming around the aquarium. I had bought the parents for two dollars each and now I had an aquarium of their offspring potentially worth over two hundred dollars. Before I learned the hardships of trying to raise these babies, I thought of selling my family the idea of going into the fish-breeding business.

We also used to watch the mating of guppies, swordtails, and platyfish, which bear their young alive, and we saw them giving birth. It was fun to read and discuss all the aspects of these various modes of reproduction. It made it easier on those mother-daughter talks, too.

Throughout high school, fish were on my mind. No matter what topic we were told to write about for our English class compositions, I could usually slant the subject to bring in fish. Biology was my favorite course, for in it I learned fundamentals about plants and animals that made me understand more about my pets. I could now visualize what took place in that bubble nest from the time the male fish blew the eggs into the bubbles until the time two hundred dollars' worth of tiny tails appeared.

When I started at Hunter College, I had to cut down my menagerie a little. I didn't have as much spare time to devote to its upkeep and besides we had taken an apartment with grandma, and the space for my pets became limited to my room only. But alas, they didn't always stay there. The worst offender was my largest snake, named Rufus, a black Racer. Rufus was always getting me into trouble. I was late for school several times because we awoke in the morning to find Rufus missing from his cage and grandma wouldn't let me leave the house until he was located. He'd manage to sneak out of an opening you'd swear wouldn't accommodate him. Grandma was getting fed up. "You be sure Rufus is securely locked in his cage when Mrs. Bertie comes today." Mrs. Bertie was grandma's bosom friend but she had a bad heart and was very much afraid of snakes. We didn't tell her we kept them or she'd never have come to visit grandma. I checked Rufus' cage and to be doubly sure, I locked the door to my room.

Grandma and Mrs. Bertie chatted merrily that afternoon and I hung around eating cookies and little cakes, usually hidden away but today being served in honor of our visitor. Suddenly, I saw grandma turn pale. I followed her look and froze to my seat. Beside Mrs. Bertie's foot, nonchalantly crawling out from under the chair, was Rufus.

Grandma collected her wits quickly. "Genie, go pick up that old black rope under Mrs. Bertie's chair." Our visitor looked down casually, moved her foot away slightly, and went on chatting to grandma as I lifted Rufus up and carried him out of the room.

In my second year at Hunter, some reporters interviewed me about my animal collection, and asked to see some of my snakes. "Surely you'd be afraid to put that brown snake around your neck," one of them challenged me. "Oh no," I answered. This was my first experience with reporters. Although I had never thought of doing it before, I wrapped my pet around my neck. He twined his head and tail together and hung there comfortably. The reporters uttered exclamations of praise and I beamed proudly. Suddenly a flash went off. Someone had taken a picture.

The next day an enlargement of my pose appeared in the Long Island *Daily Star*. The accompanying article read, "Hunter girl starts new fad in necklaces." First I was dumfounded; then, when a "friend" asked when I was going to join the circus, I felt embarrassed and guilty about my thoughtless showing off.

The following day, I was called out of my German class and told to report to the Dean. When I entered her office she asked firmly, "Are you our Hunter girl who wears slimy snakes around her neck?"

I explained that I didn't use them as necklaces and that they weren't slimy. But of the latter, she could not be convinced.

"Have you ever touched a snake?" I asked her. She admitted that she hadn't but after some persuading she consented to a test. I brought her one of my little, smooth green snakes—a beautiful emerald-colored creature that had even won the affection of my grandmother. When the Dean observed its lovely color, its large, bright, brown eyes; touched its skin and felt its dry, velvety texture and the caressing manner in which these warmth-loving animals respond to the touch of a gentle hand —she changed her mind about snakes. I went on with my snake collecting with the Dean's approval.

At college, naturally, I majored in zoology. I wanted to become a professional zoologist, preferably an ichthyologist. I had talked about this for years but as I embarked on serious preparation for it, my mother expressed some concern. "Maybe you'd better take a few courses in typing and shorthand on the side. In case you don't find a job like Dr. Beebe's when you finish college, you might get a start as some famous ichthyologist's secretary." But school, homework, and my hobby didn't leave me time for side courses and she didn't press me further.

I took every course in zoology and those related to it that I could possibly fit into my program. As most of these courses were supplemented with extra hours of laboratory training, I had one of the longest schedules in school. But I always felt that science majors had a more interesting time than the other students, who learned their material almost solely from lectures and books. We were closer to our work. We didn't just read that if a purple-eyed fly is mated to a normal-eyed fly, all their offspring will have normal eyes, but those of the second gener-

ation will have a ratio of three normal-eyed flies to every purple-eyed fly. We bred the flies in bottles, followed their life
cycles for two generations, and counted the types of offspring
to confirm this remarkably consistent ratio that exemplified one
of the most fundamental laws of heredity. And it applied to
fish as well as flies. It was worth the extra hours to be able to
watch and control living phenomena right under our noses as
part of our schoolwork.

Anatomy laboratory sessions, though we dealt mostly with
nonliving material such as animal cadavers and sections through
their organs, were equally interesting. We understood the
movements of a cat's leg because we had dissected and studied
all the bones, muscles, and nerves involved. Each of us had our
own cat cadaver. At the end of the semester, I got permission
from the teacher to take my cadaver home.

Ross, a young friend of mine who was studying art, had been
studying the anatomy of animals from art book illustrations.
We planned to get together and make sketches of the real
specimen I had. But grandma reacted rather violently when she
saw what I had brought home in the large oilskin bag which
was the shroud of my specimen. She still hadn't recovered from
the shock of finding in the icebox, a few weeks before, a dead
monkey that a kind pet-shop owner had let me have. She laid
down the law this time. "No more dead animals in this house."

Before I abandoned my parcel I decided to consult with my
artist friend.

"What have you got in the bag?" Ross asked as he let me
into his apartment.

"It's the cat. Grandma won't let me keep it."

"That's O.K.," he said obligingly, "We can keep it here. I've got room in my closet. My mother won't mind."

So for several weeks, Ross and I got together in our spare time and made sketches of the cat's anatomy. The relationship of all its parts became very clear in my mind as we leisurely drew and discussed each organ in turn. Ross showed me techniques in shading and perspective that made the layers of muscles stand out in my drawings.

I noticed that Ross kept the oilskin bag in the back of his closet behind some boxes, and when we had it out, he was always careful to close the door of his room. "Does your mother know about the cat?" I finally asked him.

"I hadn't mentioned it to her yet, but she wouldn't care."

"What about the smell?" The cat itself wasn't bad but its embalming fluid somehow combined with the oilskin bag to form a rather strong odor. Ross explained that with all the oils and paints he used in his work, the smell from the cat blended in so you could hardly notice it. But I couldn't enjoy our sketching sessions after that; Ross' mother always greeted me so sweetly and then we would close the door of Ross' room on her and bring out the corpse we were hiding in the closet.

I felt better when we decided to turn our model over to the Department of Sanitation.

During summer recesses from Hunter, I went to the University of Michigan's Biological Station, located in the woods of northern Michigan where field courses in zoology and botany were conducted. We went out to collect fish and snakes as part of our school "work."

There I shared a cabin with another zoology student and it was the most normal thing for us to bring home snake eggs and hatch them on our dining table. My roommate, Norma, tamed a wild ground squirrel that lived nearby and soon it was sharing our cabin and food. We were popular with ground squirrels and other students because we always had a supply of crunchy almond cookies that Nobusan sent us in large boxes from his restaurant all the while we were away from home. He also wrote me letters in Japanese but it took me days to figure out the latest news from Fuji's.

Norma also went to Hunter. We were both on the swimming team and our cabin in Michigan was next to Douglas Lake where we could keep in training. It was a glorious vacation for us. We loved every minute of the field courses that gave us the chance to study animals in nature. I felt such a feeling of freedom, living in what seemed to be the wilds after being brought up completely in the city.

Perhaps there was just one moment, at the beginning of each day that we took ornithology, that didn't agree with us. I was never one to get up with the birds but to get up *before* the birds, so as to be in the field by the time they were getting up, was a part of ornithology I didn't take to readily. It was, in fact, a dreadful moment when the alarm went off at 3:45 A.M. and Norma and I would awake hoping for the sound of a heavy rain that would cancel the class trip. But the rest of the day, once we could drag ourselves out of bed to face the still black morning, was so rewarding that the following summer we found ourselves signing up for the course in advanced ornithology which, because of its longer field trips, sometimes started even earlier.

We often began ornithology days wondering why any sane person cared what birds were singing at that hour of the morning. But as the day progressed and we listened to hermit thrushes trilling in the woods and the chorus of other songsters that late risers never hear, and the smell of bacon and eggs frying and coffee boiling came through the woods and hunger knocked out the last feeling of sleepiness—it was very fine indeed to be taking a course in ornithology. Those were the only days I ever ate breakfast and watched the sun rise with all traces of sleep gone.

Summers of practical field study in Michigan, supplementing our years at Hunter, made us feel that we had a great advantage over students who had no opportunity to take other than the formal schedule of courses.

But my mother was right. When I finished college, jobs like Dr. Beebe's weren't waiting for me. The Second World War was well under way. Industries were booming with war work and there was a shortage of men. The Want Ads were filled with opportunities for young and inexperienced majors in chemistry, physics, and mathematics, but there were very few offers for zoologists. And inexperienced zoologists with a mere college degree seemed to be a dime a dozen. Employers looking for biologists could afford to be choosey and they reviewed applicants for the number of degrees, years of experience, and number of scientific publications that the applicants had to their credit.

I decided to try my hand at chemistry, to earn enough money to pay for graduate studies in zoology. I was able to get a job as a chemist at Celanese Corporation, in their plastic research laboratories in Newark. It was a novel experience, working in a large industrial laboratory where the greatest discovery you could make was one that would make the most money for the company.

I worked more than fifty hours a week and my pocketbook seemed to overflow on pay days. But at night I went to New York University where the expensive lab courses burned holes in my pocketbook on registration days.

Norma also worked at Celanese and we took courses at N.Y.U. together. Since we had to commute to work, eat on the run to make our classes, and study when and if we could fit it in, we regularly had less sleep than the nights before our ornithology classes at Michigan.

In those hectic days, we shared our first flunk in zoology. Our professor of endocrinology had an odd way of lecturing with his eyes fixed on the ceiling so that we didn't feel ashamed if we lost track of what he was saying. He had a lullabying, monotonous voice and often lectured while showing slides in the darkened classroom.

At the end of the term, Norma and I found ourselves with very inadequate notes in this course. A good-natured, efficient-

looking girl in our class took pity on us and lent us her beautifully typed lecture notes. But the last few days, as Norma and
I crammed for the final exam, we realized what an awful lot
we had missed. We made little sense out of our friend's notes
but had no time to question them and could only memorize
them blindly. In the end, we flunked the exam and so did the
girl with the beautiful lecture notes.

The graduate course I never failed to sit through wide awake
was a course in ichthyology. Our professor, who had been the
Director of the Aquarium at Battery Park until it was discon-
tinued, was now the Curator of the Department of Fishes at the
American Museum of Natural History—Norma's and my old
hangout in the days when we could spare week ends to browse
in the halls of this magnificent building. The ichthyology class
was held at the museum. After lectures we could go down to
the Hall of Fishes and study the exhibits that dealt with the
lecture for the day. The whole atmosphere was stimulating,
and Professor Breder's wide background and personal research
with fishes enlarged my own horizons. Later it was he who
sponsored my research project needed for a Master's degree,
and introduced me to plectognaths—that group of fishes I was
to become intimately acquainted with and eventually seek in
some of the most remote places in the world.

It is hard to define the plectognaths as a group without going into technical anatomical details. But they are a closely related group of some nine families of rather slow swimmers
with small gill openings, who live mostly in tropical marine

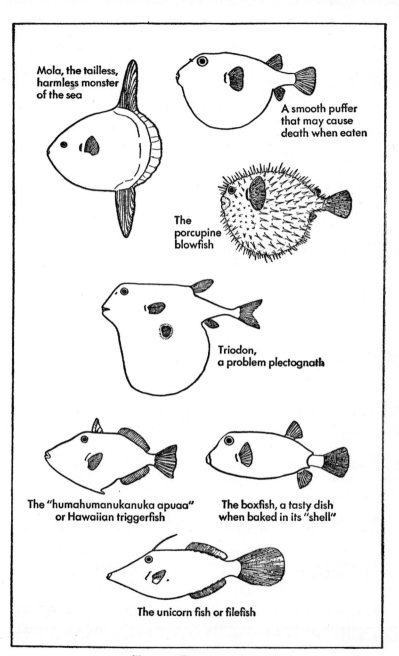

Mola, the tailless, harmless monster of the sea

A smooth puffer that may cause death when eaten

The porcupine blowfish

Triodon, a problem plectognath

The "humahumanukanuka apuaa" or Hawaiian triggerfish

The boxfish, a tasty dish when baked in its "shell"

The unicorn fish or filefish

TYPICAL PLECTOGNATHS

waters near coral reefs. Aside from that they seem to represent the most heterogeneous assortment of bizarre marine creatures that a taxonomist could possibly group together.

Did you ever hear of a fish without a tail? Only the Order Plectognathi can boast of such an oddity. If you see a tailless monster way out at sea, floating motionlessly on its side, basking in the sun and looking like a small barren island—then you are looking at a molid, or what is more popularly called an ocean sunfish.

Perhaps you have pulled a fish out of the water on your line and suddenly found that it was blowing up like a balloon and croaking like a frog. That's a common plectognath to be sure and can be caught right off Long Island. But have you seen its tropical relative that not only blows up but lifts hundreds of long spines all over its body like an aggravated porcupine?

You've probably heard the melodious Hawaiian lament about the lonesome little Hawaiian, the homesick island boy, who wants to go back to his fish and poi and his little grass shack in Kealakahua, Hawaii "where the humahumanukanuka apuaa goes swimming by." But do you know what a humahumanukanuka apuaa is? The author of the song might just as easily have called this swimmer by its scientific name, *Rhinecanthus aculeatus,* which has the same number of letters. It is a plectognath that grunts like a pig, carries a triggerlike locking mechanism on its back, and will stick its head in a hole like the proverbial ostrich when you frighten it. It is only one of the many gaudy-colored species of the family of triggerfishes.

Triggerfishes are closely related to filefishes, a group degenerated from triggerfishes where the "trigger" has been reduced to a "file" among other things. Some filefishes have the unusual habit of standing on their heads.

Then there is the fellow that no one can figure out. There is only one thing certain about the weird *Triodon bursaris*—that it is a plectognath. What group of plectognaths it is related to is a mystery. It has teeth which are a cross between the simple blowfishes and the porcupine fishes, but its body has a gigantic folding purse which makes it like no other fish known. So scientists put it in a family all by itself. This orphan of plectognaths is extremely rare. Less than a dozen specimens have ever been found, yet because of its unusual characteristics, it has attracted attention from the first time it was pulled up. It seems like the missing link between two missing groups of plectognaths.

In the West Indies, the boxfish is considered a *pièce de résistance*, when baked in its "shell." But plectognaths as a group are not prized for their food value. In the Caroline Islands, there is a blowfish that grows to over three feet. Its flesh is delicious eating but, as any Islander can tell you, makes a risky meal for its roe can cause a horrible death. In fact almost every family in the plectognath group is suspected of having some poisonous members.

Dr. Charles M. Breder, Jr., a mechanical wizard on the side, was interested in the puffing mechanism of blowfishes. He told me that very little was actually known about the anatomy and evolutionary development of their unusual puffing behavior. He encouraged me to look into this problem, letting me make dissections and anatomical studies of the valuable specimens at the museum and giving me lab space where I pumped up the stomachs of fresh blowfishes. He discussed my work with me, guiding me with his criticisms in a manner which made me feel more like his colleague than his student. He said my results and anatomical drawings comparing the digestive systems of plectognaths and showing the relationship to the puffing mechanism were worth publishing. Later when he combined my final Master's thesis with the publication of his own studies and my name appeared as co-author, my pride was as inflated as the blowfish.

2

Underwater off Southern California

"Hubbs may be the most famous ichthyologist in the country, but he's a regular fellow. Go up and speak to him. You won't mistake him; he looks like a cross between a senator and a chow," Jan, the fish artist, told me.

At the annual convention of the Society of Ichthyologists and Herpetologists held in Pittsburgh that year, a mutual friend introduced me to Dr. Carl L. Hubbs. I could see some resemblance to Jan's description. Dr. Hubbs was a robust man of good height. He stood straight, dignified, and "wore" a brief case as if it were a part of his attire. His brown hair stood up straight in a crew cut and there were no signs of graying, although he must have been close to fifty unless he started publishing scientific papers before he left his crib. The sharp lines of his rather bushy eyebrows gave the appearance of a slight scowl and the downward sloping lids of his small brown eyes gave his face a somewhat sad expression when you looked at him closer. When he looked at you without his glasses, as he did when we first met, he lifted his eyebrows and his eyes became bigger, then his brows knitted as he scrutinized you.

It was at a party of Jan's that evening that almost broke the seams of her apartment (she had invited almost every member of the convention to "drop in for a drink and bring your friends" and they all did) that I got to see the lighter side of Dr. Hubbs. His unpredictable laughter fairly exploded in the smoke-filled room. He was the life of the party. The shortage of chairs gave him the opportunity to teach everyone a handkerchief game that he said he had learned from geisha girls in Japan, and soon he had all of us sitting around the floor snatching handkerchiefs from each other's hands.

But I was to learn that Dr. Hubbs was as serious at his work as he was jovial at his play.

It was an exciting surprise to receive a letter from him late that summer, asking if I would like a job as his part-time research assistant. It would give me time also to start working toward a Ph.D. degree at the University of California where Dr. Hubbs was professor at its Scripps Institute of Oceanography at La Jolla.

They were hurried days that followed. For the first time I was lifting my roots out of New York and moving them across the continent. I didn't have enough for train fare but luckily I was able to join a share-the-ride trip with a friend of a friend. There were three of us, all anxious to get across country as fast as possible. We drove day and night and reached California in four hectic days. Oh, for a good night's sleep in a bed! But my first night at La Jolla, the grunions, fishes that at the peak of tides ride the waves in to shore to bury their eggs in moist sand, were still mating on the beach and at midnight Dr. and Mrs. Hubbs and I went out with lanterns to take inventory.

I learned to my delight that Dr. Hubbs was an enthusiastic swimmer. The day after I arrived, we swam out a quarter of a mile together to play with a school of porpoises. The porpoises came leaping toward us. I was thrilled but also a little afraid. "Be sure to shake hands with them as they pass," Dr. Hubbs called out. But when they came close, their graceful leaping forms disappeared into the ocean and we didn't see a trace of them until they reappeared far on the other side of us.

As Dr. Hubbs' assistant, one of my jobs was counting the fin rays and vertebrae of hundreds of spiny cottid fishes—all of the same species. It was tedious, often monotonous work but it gave a solid example of such important evolutionary terms as "variation within a species" and "levels of speciation." Dr. Hubbs was careful to see I had ample time for my class studies. I was taking his course in Marine Vertebrates as well as others in Physical Oceanography and the Chemistry of Sea Water. Besides lectures at the Institute, our classes frequently consisted of going to sea on the Institute's ship where we learned to operate a dredge, take sextant readings, soundings, bottom samples, water samples, and temperatures at different depths in the sea.

I also had a little research problem of my own. Dr. Hubbs brought me a "swell" shark he had caught at sea. "I tried to bring it back alive so you could see it swell up, but it was a rough day. It got seasick on the way home and passed out."

Outside of plectognaths, swell sharks are the only group of fishes that blow up. No one had ever described the puffing mechanism of the swell shark and so I started studying its anatomy. As in the plectognath balloon fishes, I found that the puffing apparatus of this shark is also part of the digestive system. It is actually the stomach, which has highly elastic walls that distend.

It is a common misbelief that puffing fishes normally blow up by inhaling air. This idea probably came about because we usually observe a fish blow up when we pull it out of the water, where it has no alternative than to give its defense reaction by gulping down air. But in its normal habitat, where this behavior developed to its apparently useful stage, puffing fishes blow up by taking in water.

When frightened or annoyed, a blowfish gulps the water (or air, should it be in this abnormal environment) down its gullet and into its stomach. The part of the stomach that connects with the intestine has a strong ringlike muscle that closes off this connection and prevents the water from running right through and out the other end of the fish. The front part of the stomach also has a strong muscle which closes between each gulp, as we would close the neck of a balloon between puffs.

This must be a very effective mechanism. Imagine yourself a big fish chasing a normal-looking small fish. You think it will easily slip into your big mouth. You open your mouth to swallow it, when lo, it gets bigger and bigger and you have to open your mouth wider and wider. Finally you find yourself snapping at a smooth round ball (have you ever ducked for smooth round apples in a tub?) or else your prey has turned into a pin cushion with needles sticking out in all directions. Or maybe the croaking and grinding noises this little fish made while distorting its body to twice the size you thought it was discouraged you from the start.

SWELL SHARK

Yes, it's not hard to see how these slow-moving blowfishes have survived and spread all over the world.

Now the swell shark, which uses a basically similar method to inflate its body, presents a rather different question. Who wants to eat these sharks in the first place? When you visualize the sea beast who might—it doesn't seem likely that a blown-up belly would stop it. It was a matter of routine dissection to learn *how* a swell shark blows up, but *why* it does is still a problem open to students of fish behavior.

Dr. Hubbs combined his love for swimming with his love for studying fishes and he urged me to do the same. So I had my first try at using a face mask

We swam underwater among the rocky reefs just north of the Institute. The glass plate in the mask made everything so clear, it was like looking into an aquarium. Dr. Hubbs lifted his head out of the water, "Dive down and follow me." I did and he led me to a cavernous part of the reef where I saw the head of a large greenish fish looking out at us. Suddenly I recognized it as a moray eel and I shot to the surface. Dr. Hubbs came up laughing.

"Isn't that big moray dangerous?" I asked.

"First of all, that was only a little fellow. He just looked big through your face mask—everything underwater looks at least a third larger than it actually is. These morays won't harm you if you watch out and don't get too close or careless." So I learned one of the most fundamental facts about most of the so-called dangerous fishes.

La Jolla proper is actually a few miles south of Scripps Institute of Oceanography. I was in a restaurant gobbling down a hamburger sandwich with a fat slice of raw onion but my stomach, tight with excitement, gave little digestive assistance. Today I was going to walk on the sea bottom in a diving helmet. Dr. Hubbs had practically promised it. I hurried out of the luncheonette, loaded a bag of groceries on my motor scooter, and putt-putted through La Jolla on my way back to the Institute. It was always nicer going back. Downhill most all the way, the weak motor of the scooter never conked out. I could ride along easily and take in the beautiful coastal scenery of southern California. You could see the Institute from town. Its white buildings sparkled in the sunlight, and today, at the end of the pier, the Institute's research ship, the *E. W. Scripps,* lay at anchor waiting for us.

A diver who had worked with the Navy was going to give instructions and a diving lesson to four of the men studying at Scripps. Dr. Hubbs, an experienced helmet diver, was going to use the helmet to explore the kelp beds off La Jolla and I tagged along as his general assistant, hoping to have a chance to use the helmet too.

When we were anchored off the kelp bed, our instructor from the Navy gave us a briefing on the signals used underwater—standard Navy signals for helmet divers with no system for speaking to the ship.

One tug on the signal cord by the diver tells the tender, "I'm all right." Two tugs mean, "Give me more line, I'm going farther away." Three tugs tell the tender, "Take up slack in line, I'm coming in closer." And four tugs mean, "Danger, pull me up fast."

"Be sure you have these signals straight," the instructor cautioned. "And remember, the job of the tender is very important and every diver should learn to tend lines to get the feel of the signals from both ends. The tender should give the line a single tug every now and then which asks the diver if he's all right and then the diver should answer to reassure the tender. The bottom here is about twenty-eight feet, which means you'll have nearly two atmospheres of pressure in your lungs from breathing the air we pump to you at that depth. If for any reason you have to 'slip' your helmet and come up without it, be sure to let that compressed air out of your lungs as you're rising. There's a valve on the right side to regulate the amount of air you're getting."

"O.K., who wants to go first?"

I looked at Dr. Hubbs anxiously but he motioned to me to wait.

The first man went down. He wore just bathing trunks and sneakers. He walked down the ladder on the side of the ship and when he was up to his neck in water, they lowered the heavy helmet onto his naked shoulders. He was down only a few minutes but several of us took turns tending his line, at least long enough to give it one tug and get his answer, which was hard to distinguish from the pull and bounce of the ship. He came up wide-eyed. "The water's a bit cold and eerie down there but it was wonderful."

The second man wore slacks and a shirt, and he said he wanted to stay down longer. But when he reached the bottom of the ladder, some feet underwater, he climbed up again. "I'm afraid my sinuses can't take it." He was really a disappointed man.

"Let Genie have a try," I heard Dr. Hubbs saying to the instructor, and in a few minutes I was on the ladder, lowering myself into the cold water while the weight of the helmet flattened the goose bumps on my shoulders.

But once the helmet was completely submerged, it rested more comfortably. When I reached the bottom rung of the ladder I could see under the ship's hull and I glanced around. I was over a thick bed of kelp. The ends of the long strands of orange-brown seaweed reached up through the murky green water just to my feet, as if I were standing on the tops of sinuous trees in this strange underwater forest. Every now and then, the kelp tops bent in unison like long grass in an open field when a breeze passes. I could feel the shift in the water current too. It was like a cold draft and I wished I had worn more than just my bathing suit, for some clothing, though it be soaking wet, is considerable protection against the winds of the underwater world.

I grabbed the rope hanging beside the ladder and let myself slide down it into the heart of the kelp forest. I started walking along the sandy bottom of the sea among the waving kelp fronds that now stretched high above my head. The ship's keel looked far overhead. What a lot of fish down here and how close they came to inspect this slow-moving intruder they did not seem to fear. One bold fish came right up to my helmet and looked in at my face. "Shoo," I said, rather startled. A strong and unpleasant odor hit me in the face. The klunking sound of the air pump filled the helmet along with the close air in the small space that now had the smell of rubber from the life line mixed in sordid combination with something else. I finally identified it. "Well, Genie, I hope you remember not to eat onions with your hamburger before your next dive."

The kelp was thick around me. It was dark and cold and indeed eerie. I headed for a more open sandy area, shimmering in filtered sunlight. I felt a tug on the signal cord and gave one back. But they tugged again and again, in spite of my answers, until finally I gave one big pull, almost falling over in the process—and then the line was still. It took more force than I thought, to make them feel my answer.

Everything was fine now except for my breathing. The rubber-onion scented air was heavy and I was breathing with difficulty. I opened the air-regulating valve a little and, with relief, felt the air grow fresher. But still it seemed that breathing under two atmospheres of pressure and walking with this clumsy weight on my head was far from comfortable.

The sand suddenly moved under my foot and a flounder scurried out of my way. There was a dark mass ahead of me and I headed toward it, but my line was taut and held me back. I backed up a few steps to get a better grip, and then I gave two heavy yanks on my signal cord. I felt a loosening as the tender obligingly gave me more line. Walking toward the dark mass, I got close enough to see that it was a cluster of rocks. It had holes in it like windows, and lovely lavender sea anemones, abalones, shellfish, and sponges decorated it. It was like coming across a gingerbread house in this water forest but there was no telling what witch of the sea might live here. I decided not to go too close. I walked around it. The kelp thinned out and sharp rocks protruded from the sandy bottom. I walked on, poking at brown starfish, sea cucumbers, and a keyhole limpet with a black velvet mantle covering its whole shell except for the "keyhole." I tried to catch some of the close-swimming fish in my hand.

Suddenly I looked up and saw the kelps far away bending toward me in a low bow. The bow traveled quickly forward through the kelp bed and I braced myself, bending my helmet and leaning forward as one would to buck a strong wind. And it was well I did, for a strong underwater current swept by with great force. I was mentally patting myself on the back for being so well prepared when I was completely knocked off my feet, almost losing the helmet, by the returning current that had sneaked up from behind me. I learned to expect and respect the return and about-face of tidal currents. The sea was growing rougher but I went on, spellbound by the magic all around me.

Soon I was not just breathing heavily but actually gasping. I opened the air valve some more but it didn't help. I opened it more and more until it seemed to be completely open, but the gasping grew worse. My head started getting groggy and I realized something was very wrong. I hadn't exchanged signals with my tender for some time. Better give those four tugs. I reached for the signal cord. It hung loosely down my side to the sea floor. I turned around in panic and saw to my horror the slack line, yards and yards of it, lying along the sea floor in the meandering path I'd come along. It looked like a long snake coiled around the rocks and the footholds of the kelp. I lifted it up and pulled but a coil caught on a rock. I started to retrace my steps back toward the ship as fast as the clumsy helmet would let me move. It was like trying to run in a nightmare, where your legs will only move in slow motion.

My breath grew shorter, my eyes burned, and my head felt numb. I seemed to struggle along miles of my lifeless life line before I finally saw the hull of the ship, still some distance away, but the line was taut here. My arms and legs were turning to rubber but with a last splurge of strength I gave one good tug. Then I felt myself fainting.

The feeling of fear had left me and a sweet sickness seemed to have replaced it. Slap-happily I thought of the irony of the situation—the meaning of my last desperate tug for help—I'm all right.

I had fallen to my knees, kneeling over in the sand. In this tipped position, water began coming into my helmet. It was cool and refreshing and knocked some sense into my stupid head. I slipped the rest of the heavy helmet off and let the buoyancy of my body carry me upward. Up . . . up . . . through the green atmosphere like a balloon and with little more sensitivity. My mouth had opened involuntarily to gasp in whatever medium was available, air or water, like a blowfish in a desperate situation. But I could take nothing in. The air in my lungs came gushing out in one long continuous belch as the surrounding pressure decreased.

When I hit the surface, I saw a shower of men dive over the side of the ship. Dr. Hubbs, wearing frog's feet, reached me first. I got a glimpse of his worried face and felt his strong hand grab my hair and tow me toward the ship.

They wrapped me in blankets and the cook brought me a cup of hot coffee. "What happened?" they wanted to know. I told them about the air seeming insufficient and opening the valve to let more in. "Just like a girl to screw the valve the wrong way and cut off her air," someone remarked. But Dr. Hubbs and the instructor were checking the helmet and found the valve open fully. The air line just above the helmet had been recently mended with a garden hose attachment and this had come loose. I had been losing most of the air pumped to me before it had reached the helmet.

"It's an awful thing to have happen on your first dive," Dr. Hubbs said sympathetically. "There's only one way to help erase such an experience."

And so, when the helmet was fixed and after a short rest which didn't allow my fears to become too deeply rooted, I went down again. This time, as with the dozens of helmet dives I have done since, with no mishaps or onion-scented air.

3

Platyfish and Swordtails

In 1947, the U.S. Fish and Wildlife Service was planning to survey the fisheries possibilities around the Philippine Islands. They were looking for an oceanographic chemist who had some experience with fish. The strange combination of my training in chemical research at Celanese and Cornell Medical School, the courses I was taking at Scripps Institute of Oceanography, and my work with fish gave me just the requirements needed.

I didn't like to leave Scripps but it was an unusual opportunity—a chance to go to the Philippines where the waters abounded with plectognaths and to be a scientist on a fisheries program at what seemed to me a grand salary. Several people were surprised that a girl had been hired for the job. Then it was called to someone's attention in Washington that I was the only female scientist on the program. Some commotion

followed. I got as far as Hawaii but my passport was mysteriously delayed because, they told me, the FBI had to check my
Oriental origin and connections. As far as I know they are still
checking. They never did tell me I was cleared. After weeks of
waiting, I accepted my fate and handed in my resignation to
waiting hands. They hired a man in my place.

If a fish enthusiast has to be stranded in a strange place while
being investigated, no place could be better than Hawaii. I
watched the humahumanukanuka apuaa swimming around in
the Waikiki Aquarium along with the other fishes native to
the Pacific tropical waters. The Director of the Aquarium let
me dissect the fish that died there. There was a convenient
little laboratory, maintained by the University of Hawaii, just
back of the Aquarium. I had the chance to study the puffing
apparatus of a special group of tiny tropical puffers never
studied before. I wrote a paper describing their modifications
of this mechanism and tried writing a "key" to the Hawaiian
plectognath fishes to help in the identification of all the species
known from there. Besides the specimens from the Aquarium,
I was given access to the huge preserved fish collection at the
Bishop Museum. And so I divided my "waiting time" between
these two absorbing places while enjoying a taste of unfor-
gettable Hawaiian hospitality.

I bought my own face mask and started "goggling" underwater. The Director of the Fisheries research work in Hawaii
was the first man I ever saw shoot a fish underwater. We went
to the northwest side of Oahu in the University's boat with the
Professor of Zoology. They were studying some schools of tuna

in this region that had suddenly become infested with a parasite which was ruining the commercial value of these prized food fish. We went several miles out to sea to track down a school —flocks of sea birds, feeding at the water surface, gave us our first clue as to where we might find a school of tuna. When we hit the school we steered the boat right into it, threw out some "chum" to keep the fish close, and then pulled specimens aboard with lines and dissected out dozens of coiled up worms that marred and softened the otherwise fine, firm tuna "meat."

On our way back, we anchored near a coral reef for a swim to refresh our hot and fishy-smelling bodies. Professor Hiatt and I wore face masks and the Fisheries Director, Vernon Brock, who ordinarily wore strong glasses, had special underwater goggles with ground lenses. Mr. Brock also wore frog's feet and had a spear.

The water was blue and incredibly clear. I swam around near the surface, looking down at the magnificent reef below. I watched Mr. Brock dive to almost forty feet while he explored the cavernous reefs among which thousands of gorgeous tropical fish were living. Then slowly, with the maneuvers of an expert underwater swimmer, Mr. Brock followed a huge green parrot fish and after a quick thrust he had it flapping on his spear as he swam back to the surface. It was a thrilling capture to watch but even though I hadn't wanted to miss a moment of it, I had been forced to lift my head out of the water briefly several times during Mr. Brock's single-breath dive. I vowed that someday I would learn to use a spear and catch fish this way in their own environment. In comparison, how dull it is to sit up in the airy world and pull a fish out of the water on a line!

My weeks in Hawaii flew by quickly.

Then I had to return to New York. My education was still unfinished but I had fortunately received a wonderful offer from Professor Myron Gordon, a fish geneticist of international fame, to work as his research assistant at the American Museum of Natural History. He wished to turn over to me a research problem which he said I could develop into a doctoral thesis. He also offered to sponsor my graduate studies at New York University.

Now that I think back, I realize the FBI actually did me a good turn. I'm not sure I would have been able to buckle down to working for a doctor's degree after several years in the Philippines. The longer you put off graduate studies, the harder it is to find the time and enthusiasm to go back to school.

In the field of science, a Ph.D. degree is handy to have though not absolutely necessary. One of the most brilliant and accomplished ichthyologists in this country never went to college, although later he became a university professor. But a person without a formal education has a more difficult time proving his worth, especially when applying for a position. A Ph.D. among your qualifications helps start things out on the right foot. I hoped to get this degree—my career had enough other disadvantages for a woman.

Women scientists have to buck some difficulties when it comes to field work but I had one decided advantage. A man in my position often has a family to support and is not free to travel. I was independent and free to go anywhere and do anything I liked, and there was only my own neck to risk.

When I had finished college, my mother remarried. My stepfather is a man I've loved for years—the proprietor of the tiny Japanese restaurant who used to slip me little wooden boxes containing Oriental delicacies to take home on those Saturdays when I visited the Old Aquarium at Battery Park. I don't know if my mother had postponed her marriage until then because of me. I think I would have resented sharing her with someone any time before—I had become so used to the selfish idea that everything she did was mainly for me. But when the time came for me to be on my own, when I wanted to take advantage of opportunities in any part of the world, she became Nobusan's wife and I didn't need to worry about leaving her alone.

She has never asked me for anything in return for all the years she gave me. Any time I visit her she is overjoyed to see me but she never makes demands on my time asking that I come to see her more often. And when I went away from home she was the only person who never complained about the scarcity of my letters. It is nice to have a mother who wears an apron with no strings attached.

My research problem at the museum centered about the reproductive behavior of platies and swordtails, the same kind of fishes that were in my first home aquarium. In the next few years my project was supported by the Department of Animal

Behavior (interested in the sexual behavior of these fishes), by the New York Zoological Society (interested in the genetics of these fishes), and finally by the Atomic Energy Commission (interested in the sperm physiology of fishes in general). This took care of my needs for living material, laboratory space, and all my expenses. I was very lucky.

The project had great appeal for me. It presented a challenge because it involved so many aspects of biology that had to be fitted together into one composition. It wasn't merely a study of two kinds of fishes. It was basically a study of one of the most stimulating biological phenomenon, evolution. It was a project in which the platy and the swordtail, two common aquarium fishes, could be used as the experimental animals to demonstrate one of the mechanisms of evolution called "sexual isolation."

Most of us who keep platies and swordtails in our homes don't usually think of them as sexually isolated from each other. Indeed, most of our aquarium specimens are not actually the pure platyfish and swordtail as found in nature. They are hybrids, domesticated breeds that commercial aquarists have cultivated into an amazing variety of colors and shapes, often more elaborate than the original natural species.

The beautiful wagtail swordtail, for example, is one of these hybrids where a strange, hidden, "enhancing" property from the swordtail is combined with the simple comet tail of the platy (a dark upper and lower edge to the tail) to form an exquisite hybrid with fine, delicate, black radiating stripes on *all* fins. Dr. Gordon first produced this geneticaly controlled

fish in his laboratory and now it is one of the most popular
varieties for home aquaria. The production of such aquarium
beauties is only an incidental sideline to Dr. Gordon's main
work which is the study of cancer in fishes.

The cancerous tissue of these fishes is so like that of humans
that it is almost impossible to tell them apart under a microscope. Dr. Gordon can control fish tumors genetically. He can
mate certain combinations of fishes and accurately predict the
number of offspring that will develop tumors. Certain platy-
swordtail combinations not only give the beautiful all-ebony
swordtail-like hybrid but also produce a black cancer, a mela-
noma similar to that most dreaded of human diseases.

But all the cancerous fishes of this group have been produced
by artificial breeding in the laboratory. Dr. Gordon has collected thousands of the pure species in the rivers of Mexico
and Honduras from which they originally come, but he has
never found one with a cancer. He has never found a hybrid.

The pure platy and swordtail species often live side by side
in the same river. They have been pulled up together in the
same net haul. What keeps them from interbreeding in nature and producing cancerous strains? They are physically ca-
pable of it. Aquarists have demonstrated this fact over and over
under domesticated conditions. Then how is it that these fishes
are sexually isolated in their natural habitat? *What is the "sexual isolating mechanism" that nature uses?*

This was my problem.

Dr. Gordon and Dr. Lester R. Aronson, the Chairman of the
Department of Animal Behavior, had already come to the

conclusion that one of the factors of the isolating mechanism involved the psychological aspect of mating. Both of these learned men followed my progress with interest and I was able to benefit from the criticisms and guidance of a geneticist and an animal psychologist in this problem—the most complicated I had ever tried to solve.

For there was no simple answer. As I began to study the material related to my problem and then work in the laboratory with the fishes, I realized I was dealing with a whole series of problems—the answers to each were like the pieces of a jigsaw puzzle which had to be properly fitted together.

One of the first steps was to study the mating behavior of the two species. Were there any differences that might contribute to a psychological block when, in nature, the fish has a choice between mating with his own species or the other? Yes, there were many small quantitative and qualitative differences in the courtship behavior of the two species. The act of copulation itself, for example, occurred less frequently but was of a longer duration and happened after a shorter courtship period among swordtail pairs than among platies. Platy males showed an odd behavior, typical during courtship, which we called "picking"—suddenly interrupting the chase after the female to pick at the floor of the aquarium in fast quivering movements—something the swordtail male never did. I had to make hundreds of observations to prove statistically the existence of these differences. I sat in the museum greenhouse —a jungle of aquaria—maintained at 90° F. and 100 per cent humidity. I put my face as close to the glass wall of my observation tank as I could get it, without disturbing the courting fish I was watching. I held an ingenious device on my lap that Dr. Aronson had set up for me. It was a keyboard on which I had worked out a "touch-type" system so that I could record everything the fish did without taking my eyes off them. The keyboard was electrically controlled and connected with a rotating graph that described, by a complicated system of forty pens, the exact sequence and duration of each behavior.

I accumulated reams of data. "What are you compiling there, the Kinsey report on fishes?" friends would ask me.

When I started my observations, a critical step in the mating of these fishes was not known. Exactly how and when did the male transfer his sperm into the body of the female in these species that bear their young alive? Many people have taken for granted that sperm transfer occurred when the male lightly touched the female's body with his rotated anal fin. This action is often seen in home aquaria. I observed it in my laboratory aquaria—sometimes a male would repeat this action a hundred times in ten minutes. Were all these true matings? It didn't seem likely to me but no one had ever been able to prove or disprove it.

Then I saw an unusual type of contact between the male and female—something that happened very rarely, usually after the fish had been isolated for many hours and then placed together. The male chased the female and suddenly the two fish seemed glued together for a period that lasted up to five seconds. This, I decided, was a true copulation and I set about to prove it.

I used a set of virgin females, observing each with a male for ten minutes and recording all that happened. Then with a tiny glass pipette, I took a small sample from the ovary of the living female by wrapping her in wet cotton and working under the microscope. In the sample I took from her, I could detect the presence of sperm from the male. If there was no sperm in the sample, I could use her over and over again until she was inseminated. There was no doubt about it when this occurred. The tiny sample in the droplet under the microscope swarmed with thousands of swimming sperm cells, each like a

A MALE PLATYFISH COPULATING WITH A FEMALE

separate animal in itself, darting across the lens field, a creature with a large head and a long wriggling tail.

I never witnessed this sight in samples from females that had merely been touched by the tip of a male's anal fin, even after this occurred hundreds of times. But after just *one* of the contacts that I called copulation, masses of sperm could be recovered from the female.

The technique of getting into the reproductive organs of a living female fish without injuring her was a useful device in other ways, and led to my most successful experiment.

A series of my tests showed that under natural conditions,

on rare occasions, it was possible for the psychological barriers of mating to break down. In such a case, a female of one species might mate with a male of the other species. But the females of platies and swordtails store sperm for months. What happens when the sperm from the two different species of males have to compete with each other to fertilize the eggs that then become "ripe" in the female's body? How could I test sperm competition under controlled experimental conditions?

The answer was by artificial insemination—something no one in this country had ever been able to do with fish. My experience using micropipettes in living females came in handy. I took the sperm from the male fish and put it into the female fish by reversing the technique I had been using to take sperm samples out of the female. My first experiment produced "test tube" fish babies.

It was an eventful day for me. Other research workers around the museum knew what I had been trying to do. They had been inquiring about the progress of my artificially inseminated females—while I waited around like an expectant father. Each day I hopefully looked at the belly of the most promising lady swordtail—a complete virgin except for the micropipette treatment. It was gradually swelling, although in fishes this is not a sure sign. But the final proof came in the form of twelve tiny babies. I felt like handing out cigars. Dr. Gordon came over to congratulate me. Others too shook my hand, half jokingly, yet half seriously, for I now had the means to attack the last major problem in my research project.

It was only a short step from there to begin the experiments on sperm competition. I used controlled amounts of sperm mixtures from the two species of males and then artificially inseminated the females. It was the first time such tests were ever made on fish. I was able to show that sperm competition between the two species does exist, and that the sperm from the male of the same species as the female has an advantage over the hybrid-producing sperm from the other species of male. Though the latter sperm be artificially inseminated in larger quantities, the former produced noticeably more offspring in the groups of births that followed.

And so the factors in the isolating mechanism of the platy and swordtail gradually revealed themselves.

This study led to similar work on other live-bearing fishes. Dr. Aronson and I spent months studying the most common and hardy of all aquarium pets—the guppy. We found that it too had a similar, rare copulatory act. With the same micropipette method for sperm detection in the female, we were able to disprove the common notion that male guppies are almost constantly "shooting" sperm into the female. With high-speed photographs, taken with an electronic flash unit, we were able to analyze in even more detail, the courtship maneuvers of these tiny, fast-moving fish.

4

Filefishes in the West Indies

I spent three years at the museum experimenting with the fresh-water platies, swordtails, and guppies. But not completely. There were interludes when I had a chance to keep in touch with marine fishes. One summer I studied at the famous Marine Biological station at Woods Hole in Massachusetts where I had a chance to work on some of the North Atlantic fishes. I also took off a few months for some trips to the West Indies to study tropical Atlantic fishes. Dr. Breder, my first mentor, was now the Director of the new Lerner Marine Laboratory on the island of Bimini. He invited me to study the plectognaths of that region which included, to my great delight, opportunities for underwater goggling.

Goggling in the beautiful clear water around Bimini had one disadvantage. Diving among the delicate lavender and canary-yellow sea fans, I would look up through the magnifying face mask and see a barracuda watching me. They were very common. The ones I met were quite small, not over three feet. But it was not unusual to find two or three of them in the water with me.

Once I was diving with a little knife with which to cut some of the sea fans loose. I wanted to dry them and bring them back to my family for souvenirs—unlike most marine animals they keep their colors well. As I was heading for the surface with two lovely fans, I met a barracuda. He didn't make a move but just looked at me calmly—with no sign of the fear that other fishes have. I felt as if a policeman had caught me stealing flowers from a park and I let the sea fans drop back to the bottom.

Eventually I got fairly used to seeing barracuda, the small ones that is, for I don't know what I would have done if a full-grown one had come along. The natives of Bimini fear them greatly and my Negro tender was more concerned than I was when I went down in a diving helmet. I'd no sooner reach bottom than Pedro would call down over the speaking system, "Better come up now, Miss Janie, dem barracudas gonna come soon."

I liked to use my face mask more than the diving helmet for most occasions. I was learning to hold my breath longer now and could go down almost as deep without the helmet which limited my movements. And too, with the face mask, I didn't have to listen to Pedro constantly urging me to get back in the boat.

Pedro was much happier when we took the boat out to collect fish by scooping up floating seaweed into nets while we stayed out of the water.

Bimini has some remarkable plectognaths. And none more remarkable than the filefishes.

Once Pedro and I caught a group of baby filefish by dipping a net into a clump of Sargasso weed that had floated toward Bimini from the Sargasso Sea. I put them alive into an aquarium in the laboratory. "Ever see these filefish go crazy?" Dr. Breder asked me. I had my first demonstration that evening.

We stumbled into the laboratory after dark. Dr. Breder carried a large flashlight but he didn't use it until we were standing in front of the aquarium with the baby filefish. Then suddenly he turned it on. The strong beam broke the darkness and went smack into the sleeping but of course open eyes of the babies. They didn't move at first—just stared blankly into the light. Then one, then another slowly started getting tipsy, falling forward and to the side. Some turned completely over. They looked like a group of performing tumblers. Finally they started spinning, faster and faster until some were turning like tops and zigzagging around the aquarium.

"They can go completely berserk and kill themselves in that glare," Dr. Breder informed me as he turned off the light and saved their lives. I wondered what Dr. Breder would do if he had to sleep with *his* eyes open and someone suddenly flashed a bright light into his face. Dr. Breder couldn't explain this strange reaction of the baby filefish around Bimini, although he had written a paper describing it in as much detail as he could.

In print he referred to the phenomenon as "locomotor disorganization." But in less technical terms, I had to agree with him, they looked as if they were going crazy.

Some days later I decided to see what else one might learn by prowling around a dark laboratory at night. I crept up to a tank in which I kept some of my larger filefish. Then I turned on my flashlight.

"What's this?" I asked myself, completely amazed at what I saw. For there in the tank where I kept a group of dark brown filefish with white, horizontal stripes—I saw a group of *white* filefish with *black, vertical stripes*.

It is not really unusual for a fish to change its color or pattern, but this was such a complete reversal that I could hardly believe I was looking at the same fish I had put into the tank during the daylight. I watched these fish carefully in all degrees of light, in the weeks that followed. But I only saw that strange pattern when I caught them "sleeping" in the dark. Their "pajama pattern" was only outdone by the change that occurred when they became highly excited. Then you saw spots before your eyes—bright orange spots all over the fish's body, and then there were no stripes in any direction.

But that doesn't exhaust the odd behavior of Bimini filefishes. Dr. Beebe was the first to point out the habit some of the filefishes have of standing on their heads. The species he observed were long and thin and this position made them resemble seaweed. He believed the behavior was mainly one of camouflage.

I had a chance to study a group of headstanders in the laboratory at Bimini. They didn't stand on their heads all the time, but when they did it was a spectacular display. This particular species had an abdominal flap which could be spread out like the tail of a peacock. When one of these fish, especially a male, executed a headstand, he also spread his skirtlike flap along with all his other fins, lifted his "file" until it stood up like a unicorn's, and vibrated his body.

A DOMINANT MALE FILEFISH DOING A "HEADSTAND"
BEFORE A RECESSIVE MALE

This happened when two males met face to face. They would both start to go into a headstand but only one would succeed fully. The other fish, usually the smaller, would fold up his fins and back out of the path of the other. I found that there was one male from which all the others backed away. Then there was a #2 male that all but #1 backed away from. And so on down the line to the poor fish that backed away

from all the others. He was the smallest and most sickly looking and soon died, as all the other fish would beat him to the
food at feeding time.

This system in fishes is remarkably similar to that first discovered in hens. My poor sickly fish who died wasn't exactly
"henpecked" but he was "headstood" by all the others.

5

The Eyes of Fishes

Fish's eyes are remarkable organs. I know of no other group of animals with optical systems of such variations.

The earliest fish had three eyes. A study of fossil fish shows a small opening in the center of the skull top. This opening once held a structure known as the *pineal eye*—a light-sensitive organ, rudiments of which still persist in fish living today.

Some people say there are fish with four eyes. *Cuatro Ojos* is the popular name of one variety of a strange fish that lives in Mexico. Not because it wears glasses—but because of something biologically more remarkable than that. Strictly speaking, Cuatro Ojos has only two eyes, but each eye is divided into two parts: the upper half has become adapted for *air* vision while the lower half can see under water. Cuatro Ojos makes good use of this unique optical arrangement to spot *all* its enemies. A small fish that lives in shallow water among tide pools, it sometimes even hops around on the land nearby. But most of the time it sits or swims at the surface of the water with its head held partly out so that just the upper halves of its eyes are in the air, where it can see what's going on above and below the surface simultaneously.

There is a little blenny fish with a similar "four-eye" arrangement. But in this creature each eye is divided so that the forward half has air vision and the rear half water vision. It is believed that this fish clings in a vertical position to the sides of water-filled potholes, with only his snout and the forward half of his eyes projecting into the air.

The fish world has its cyclopses, too. Experimental embryologists can produce cyclopean fish by subjecting embryos to special treatments at a critical stage. But, as in all vertebrates, one-eyed individuals are deformed and not characteristic of any species.

Completely eyeless fish, however, are well known among forms that inhabit rivers and lakes in dark caves and those which dwell in abyssal depths of the sea where sight is not a factor in survival.

But most fish have two eyes—though not necessarily on opposite sides of the head, as many of us know who have looked at the lopsided flounder. Flounders, members of the flatfish family, start out in life with an eye on each side of the head and swim in typical fish fashion. But as the young fish develops, a metamorphosis takes place. It starts leaning over to one side, then lying with this side on the sandy bottom; then the eye on the bottom side starts migrating across the head to the top side.

Fish don't have eyelashes. But some fish have a sort of eyelid. Certain sharks can wink and blink because they possess thin, semitransparent *nictitating* membranes which they can draw over their eyes. All other fish must spend their entire lives with their eyes open.

Have you ever stopped to wonder what it would be like to see two completely different visions simultaneously, one with each eye? That, of course, is what fish do. Our eyes focused on the same object report a single merged image to the brain; the fish's brain receives two images at once, for its eyes face in opposite directions and cannot focus simultaneously on the same object.

There are a few exceptional fish types, however, whose two eyes are on the same plane and would lead you to suspect they have binocular vision like ours. Of such are the flat-topped "stargazers" and certain "pop-eyed" fishes. Among the pop-eyed fishes the telescopic-eyed goldfish is probably the best known. Sometimes it is sold in the five-and-ten-cent stores. The most highly prized variety, however, is a rare breed perfected in China —the Celestial Telescopic "Gold" fish, a jet-black beauty lacking a back fin and having eyes which, like "stargazers," always look heavenward.

But of all the pop-eyed creatures in the animal kingdom, *Stylophthalmus* takes the prize. *Stylophthalmus* is a deep-sea fish. It was first thought to be an entirely new genus until the stages of its life cycle were found and it was discovered that

Stylophthalmus is the young form of a known, normal-eyed adult fish, *Idiacanthus*. The connection was hard to imagine before the intermediate stages were found, for the larval fish has its eyes located on the ends of incredibly long stalks—slender, flexible, wirelike protrusions from the head that allow the eyes to turn and see in all directions. As the young fish grows, the stalks gradually grow shorter until the eyes sit in their proper sockets. Then only a dissection of the long coiled optic nerves in back of the eyes of the adult could give a clue to their strange development.

Can a fish remember with its left eye something it has learned with its right? It was Dr. Roger Sperry, a neuroanatomist I met while studying at Bimini, who brought up the question.

It seemed a rather pointless question to me at first because I thought of it in terms of human capabilities—a fault of many novices in the field of animal behavior and a poor attitude in scientific reasoning, one that can obscure truth and eliminate the investigation of an important problem by giving it an easy solution but a wrong one. My first reaction was: Why naturally, if *my* left eye were covered and I saw, with only my right eye, a large and small object on the table, tasted both and learned that only one was edible, I would certainly remember which one it was when I viewed the same objects with only my left eye.

Then Dr. Sperry told me that in some experiments with pigeons, it was discovered that they could not make this simple transfer when certain parts of their eyes were tested. Birds, like fish, except for certain flat-faced forms like the owl, have eyes on opposite sides of the head and each eye sees independently of the other. When a bird wants to get a better look at you, he cocks his head to one side or the other. Fish which have no necks to turn must turn their whole bodies to one side for the same purpose. Does the bird's—or the fish's—right eye know what its left is doing?

A human may learn to play the bass part of a song on the piano with his left hand, but this does not mean that he can then play it with his right—the habit is not transferred. A fish, with its primitive brain—even more primitive than the pigeon's —and its way of registering separate optical impressions with each eye, may well lack the co-ordination necessary to transfer a visual discrimination habit from one eye to the other.

When the significance of the original question finally impressed me, I was curious to know the answer. Dr. Sperry then told me that he had planned an experiment to find out. But it was a time-consuming enterprise, too long for him to do alone in the period he was staying at Bimini. He needed someone to help him, preferably someone experienced with fish, as he had done most of his previous work with amphibians and small mammals. I was only too glad to get my fingers into the experiments.

So I divided my time between plectognaths and gobies. Dr. Sperry chose gobies because they are easy to obtain on Bimini; they live in shallow tide pools and hence tolerate stagnant water and can be kept in aquaria without running water; and finally because they usually sit on the bottom of the aquarium without swimming about and this made it easy for us to test their vision. We used twenty-nine gobies. Each had to be kept in a separate aquarium and studied individually. Dr. Sperry began by operating on them—placing a tin-foil cap over one eye or cutting one optic nerve. Then we taught each of our half-blinded fish a visual discriminating habit with its good eye.

It wasn't easy to find a good test—one in which we could be sure the fish had learned the "trick" with only his eye and not with the help of his nose, lateral line system, or any other sensory organs that might pick up clues from odors or vibrations in the water.

The test we finally used was this. We let the goby get good and hungry and then put a lure in its tank. The lure consisted of a wire that could be suspended vertically in the water above the head of the goby sitting on the bottom. At the lower end of the wire was a large piece of white glass wool. Above it, part way up the wire, we put a small piece of white meat from a shellfish.

The goby, when hunger overcome its initial fear, swam up from the bottom of the tank and started investigating the lure. One of us had to watch it carefully. If the goby once touched the glass wool, the lure was immediately taken out and the poor fish got nothing but a prick on the nose.

This sometimes went on for dozens of trials (though some of the "smarter" gobies caught on quickly) until it finally occurred to the goby to try a little farther up the wire before biting at the first white hunk it saw. Then it was rewarded. Instead of a prick on the nose, it found its mouth against some-

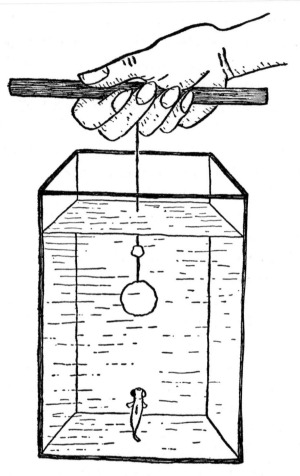

GOBY BEING TRAINED TO DISCRIMINATE VISUALLY

thing soft and good to eat and was given enough time to take
a good bite. The goby learned quickly after that and soon it was
carefully by-passing the big piece of glass wool without touching it, and going straight to the small piece of food above, which
was almost hidden by the glass wool. We kept score and when

a fish made seventeen or more correct bites out of twenty consecutive trials, we figured the fish had learned to discriminate.

To be sure it was visual discrimination we did many types of tests. One, for example, was to replace the glass wool with a big piece of the same white meat used over it. The goby still went by without touching it, straight to the smaller piece that was higher and more difficult to reach. This ruled out the chance that the fish was smelling its way to the food.

The second part of the experiment was the significant one. The good eye of each goby was now blinded—again by either a tin-foil cap or severing the optic nerve. The other eye was brought back to normal by removing the original cap or merely waiting until the optic nerve regenerated. The fish were then tested with the same lure.

"It remembered!" we exclaimed together, as the first fish zoomed right up to the food without the slightest interest in the glass wool. But as we continued, my high spirits lowered. Some of the others hesitated and then made a number of errors so that their first twenty tests gave a noticeably lower score than before. And there were a few who started all over from scratch again, getting noses pricked and no food, over and over, as if they had never seen the lure before. "Moron!" I couldn't help calling each of these as I tested them. "Why can't you remember?"

These last cases were hard to explain. To check the possibility of factors such as trauma, Dr. Sperry switched the eye cap again. With caps in the original learning position, the "morons" had no trouble discriminating between the white pieces on the wire. Switch the cap again, and they were again ignorant! It was exasperating. How could there be such a variation among individuals of the same species?

The fact that we could prove that visual transfer had taken place perfectly in only *some* of our gobies seemed inadequate to me. But Dr. Sperry, with his much greater experience and more philosophical outlook, assured me that our results were of value, nevertheless. We had opened a new branch of research in fish optics and behavior, and clear-cut solutions to complicated problems seldom result from first experiments. Especially in the field of animal behavior, there is seldom a definite "yes" or "no" answer to questions dealing with the response of animals. That is why we have statistical methods to show trends, tendencies, or chance of such and such happening.

The more I work on behavioral problems and see the problems of other workers, the less I let irregularities in my results bother me. But even today, when I pick up the publication of our results at Bimini and look through the tables and see the scores for goby #3, for example, I still ask under my breath, "Why couldn't you remember?"

Perhaps someday more experiments will be done along these lines and I'll know the answer.

6

Bronx Zoo to Hawaii

We were sitting in a large room in the administration building of the Bronx Zoo. It didn't promise to be anything special —a few speeches, committee reports, secretary's and treasurer's reports and other miscellany. It was the closing meeting, the business section, of a convention of animal psychologists. Who could have dreamed that it was the introduction to a trip to the South Seas?

My mind was wandering as the various committee chairmen gave their routine reports. And then the word "Micronesia" caught my ear and I focused attention on the speaker. Dr. Harold Coolidge, Executive Secretary of the Pacific Science Board, was telling about opportunities for a few people to study in the South Seas as part of a program entitled "Scientific Investigations in Micronesia" to be sponsored by the Office of

Naval Research. The Pacific Science Board and the Navy wanted to learn more about the numerous little islands in the Pacific which, since the end of World War II, formed the United States Trust Territory.

I came home from the meeting thinking about the romantic South Sea islands I'd read about so often—stories of poets and painters and shipwrecked sailors, travelogues, reports of expeditions. I recalled my delightful taste of Pacific coral reefs on my short visit to Hawaii two years before.

Of course I sent in an application to the Pacific Science Board. But the forecast didn't look encouraging. Experienced people who knew much about this area thought it unlikely that the Board would be willing to send a single woman around the Pacific collecting fish. Life would be too rugged in most places, tropical diseases and the heat might get a girl down, and women fishermen aren't generally encouraged—especially in Micronesia where some natives not only object to women on fishing trips, but consider them bad luck or taboo.

It was a surprise when a telephone call came through from Washington saying that the Pacific Science Board was interested in learning more about the fishes of Micronesia, particularly the identification of poisonous kinds. Could I be ready to leave for the South Pacific in a few weeks? While the almost incredible words continued to pour more details out of the telephone, scattered thoughts rushed through my mind. That very morning I had accepted an Atomic Energy Commission Fellowship which would conflict with this trip; how could I have both? I was in the midst of the last experiments for my

doctoral thesis; could I finish them in time? And—wouldn't it
be wonderful to see the South Pacific and be out of New
York during my hay fever season!

It seemed like short notice, and yet once the arrangements
were made, I couldn't wait to get started. An extension of the
Atomic Energy Commission Fellowship was granted, the American Museum of Natural History would sponsor the trip; things
worked out smoothly. I left the States on June 17, 1949, from
Alameda by jet take-off, aboard a huge double-decker Martin
Mars seaplane of the Military Air Transportation Service—
bound for Hawaii and points southwest.

In Honolulu there was a chance to do last-minute shopping,
visit old friends, and make final preparations for the trip. The
Pacific Science Board had a branch office at the Bishop Museum.
It was run by a Miss Ernestine Akers, a tall, slim, young woman
with brown bangs over a forehead that sheltered a busy mind.
Her main job was to see that the "SIM" program (as everyone
referred to Scientific Investigations in Micronesia) ran smoothly.

Although I was traveling alone, there was a feeling of se-
curity and companionship in the way my trip seemed to be
planned. In all matters connected with the arrangement of the
trip, I could depend on Ernestine while in Hawaii. She gave
me preliminary orientation, whisked me through the formalities
of getting a Navy identification card and other needed papers,
arranged for the loan of photographic equipment, etc. She was
very competent and took a big-sister interest in each of my
little problems.

Ernestine was at the airport to help me off. My baggage,

including all the extras I'd accumulated in Hawaii, weighed in at two hundred sixty pounds—just one hundred pounds over what my papers allowed. The lieutenant who was checking me in shook his head sympathetically, "If it were a matter of a *few* extra pounds, well . . . but one hundred, that's too much I'm afraid."

A huge officer, weighing at least two hundred pounds, was checking in ahead of me. Ernestine thought fast. "Suppose Miss Clark weighed two hundred pounds, you'd let her on the flight, wouldn't you?" The lieutenant admitted he would. "Well, she's only one hundred pounds," Ernestine fibbed flatteringly while I pulled in my Hawaiian food-stuffed tummy and tried to look sixteen pounds lighter.

The lieutenant scratched the back of his neck, glanced at the clock and down the line of passengers still waiting to be checked in, then looked back at the two pleading faces before him. "O.K.," he sighed and gave a crooked smile in answer to our profuse expressions of thanks.

In a few minutes I boarded another big plane and then I had a last look at Diamond Head as we flew toward the mid-Pacific.

7

Kwajalein: the Poisoners
and the Poisoned

Four hours after leaving Hawaii I awoke as the flaps were lowered for a landing. We stopped briefly at Johnston Island for refueling. You couldn't imagine a less romantic Pacific island —hardly a square mile in area, its highest point only five feet above sea level, and not a palm tree in sight. It seemed little more than just a landing strip—a resting stop for planes on long transpacific journeys.

As we took off again, I saw that the island was surrounded by coral reefs, and from little rafts men were diving into the clear water. Then I remembered that some fine reef fish collections had been made around this island. And it was here that Vernon Brock, the first person I had seen spear a fish, once had a terrible encounter with a ten-foot moray eel. He had speared the rare specimen underwater, but when trying to bring it to the surface he found it was still alive enough to attack him. He had to be quickly flown to Hawaii for hospital treatment; the arm that shielded his face when the eel attacked was crushed and lacerated. As the scene of this accident disappeared behind our plane, I decided never to try to spear a large moray eel—something I was to forget in the excitement of facing one a few weeks later.

Although I traveled a good many thousands of miles by plane during the four months of this SIM trip, I remember little of my time in the air. I usually slept if I could escape the questions of the other passengers about what a woman civilian was doing riding a military plane. The rest of the time was so exciting and there was so much to do and see at every island that on planes was the only time I could relax and sleep without feeling that I was missing something.

The next time we landed it was dark. We refueled at Kwajalein this time, then headed for Guam. What a shame to have seen so little of Kwajalein, I thought innocently, not knowing what was about to happen.

Nearly halfway to Guam the plane developed engine trouble and we had to turn back. Arriving at Kwajalein for the second time I learned my travel priority was a fancy one—equivalent to that of a Lieutenant Commander's—but I still had to wait at least two days before I could get space on another plane. Well, I had wanted to see more of this historic island anyhow.

The inhabited part of the Kwajalein atoll consisted mainly of a large Naval base where I was accommodated at the Guest House. A group of us went to visit the native village made up largely of rehabilitated natives moved from Bikini just before the Atom Bomb tests. I looked over their fishing gear—circular throw nets about fourteen feet in diameter, long-handled spears for inshore reef fishing, and hooks and hand lines to fish from their outrigger canoes farther from the shore. I wondered what kind of fish they caught.

On the way back to the Guest House I saw some tide pools on the ocean side of the atoll, and one in particular looked ideal for collecting fishes. Why not? I had brought a special solution of rotenone poison to try out on tide pools. I asked for permission to make a fish collection the next morning.

The idea was received enthusiastically; every facility on the island that I might need was generously offered. A husky Ensign Womeldorf, who liked fishing and swimming, volunteered to be my right-hand man in this enterprise. There were many other volunteers. The idea of a scientific fishing venture had the appeal of a picnic party. So that I wouldn't have to uncrate my bottles of preserving fluid, the hospital offered me a supply of formalin and alcohol. No one had died recently, so the morgue was put at my disposal for use as a laboratory to preserve and pack my anticipated fish collection.

I had had experience poisoning tide pools with Dr. Hubbs in California nearly three years before. But this was the first time I was to try it alone. I hoped I would remember how to do it correctly. There was going to be an audience. It would be awful if I got nothing. I'd be a fine example to set for an SIM scientist on this island, particularly since others had to pass through this area periodically. Well, there was only one ingredient necessary—the poison—and I had an ample supply. However, I was about to use, for the first time in marine work that I knew of, a new preparation of rotenone. Instead of the regular powder form I had a concentrated emulsion of rotenone which Pennick Company gladly supplied me gratis to test on marine fishes. It was much lighter, less bulky, and supposed to spread more easily in water than the powder. There was no reason why it shouldn't work. Dr. Gordon had recently used it successfully for collecting fresh-water fishes in British Honduras and had recommended it highly to me.

The use of poison in tide pools is an important tool of the modern field ichthyologist. It may seem unsportsmanlike compared to methods of fishing with rod and reel, even nets and traps, and especially compared to the adventurous sport of underwater spearfishing; but for scientific purposes it is of unquestionable value because of the little time spent in obtaining a large number of species. The ichthyologist is not primarily concerned with the large size and food value of the fishes he collects. Every specimen is important, from the smallest and most insignificant-looking to the largest and most spectacular. If hundreds of the same species are collected, each one is of value for population studies of that particular species.

The poisoning of fish was not invented by ichthyologists. It has been in practice for centuries by natives in widely separated parts of the tropical and subtropical world: in Asia, Africa, Pacific islands, Central and South America, and by the Indians in Southeastern United States. These natives apparently discovered independently the fish poisoning effect of plants we now classify in the *Derris* group. The primitive method is to scatter macerated parts of these plants, especially the roots, into the water where there are fish. The fish become stunned or die, but their food value is not harmed. The poison, technically known as rotenone, is now widely cultivated commercially and is used primarily as an agricultural insecticide.

Rotenone, as a fish poison, is most effective in the warm temperatures of the tropics. It takes anywhere from a few minutes to an hour for the fish to become affected. It acts by constricting the blood capillaries in the gills until their diameter is too small to allow the passage of red blood cells that come to this important area to pick up oxygen. The fish virtually suffocates to death. In sublethal doses the effect may be only temporary and the fish will fully recover.

Fortunately, other tide pool animals and plants are generally less sensitive and are not seriously damaged when we fish collectors go about our nefarious business. Aquatic vegetation is not harmed by amounts of rotenone used to kill fishes. Birds, hogs, cattle, and other mammals have been observed drinking water from rotenone-treated ponds with no ill effects. I've accidentally gulped down mouthfuls when working an hour or more in a rotenone-poisoned pool. Once I then developed a headache which may or may not have been caused by the rotenone.

And Ensign Womeldorf survived his first bath in a rotenone poisoned tide pool.

As we set out for our fish collecting, Ensign Womeldorf wanted to know how we were going about it. He probably never saw anyone go fishing before with a bottle of brown liquid.

"We'll just sprinkle some of this liquid around the pool and see what happens," I told the eager Ensign who was undoubtedly expecting something more complicated. It was about an hour before low tide, just right to give the rotenone time to have full effect at the "slack tide" period before the sea started washing in again and diluting the pool water.

Our tide pool was roughly sixty feet in diameter and was over waist deep in some places. Standing at the edge of the pool we could see a number of fish, and scurrying about the rocks and vegetation were hundreds of tiny hermit crabs; vermiform-legged starfishes and black sea cucumbers lay motionless in the sand. Here, for a short time completely isolated from the sea, was entrapped a sample of ocean life. Many of the creatures in it could be right under your nose and yet not be seen. Small fish particularly hide in holes and crevices or when exposed are so well camouflaged by their appearance and behavior that you can look directly at them without realizing it. One of the limp "leaves" of seaweed may actually be a little seahorse attached by its prehensile tail; or perhaps it is a weird angler fish with a breast fin holding onto the seaweed with a grip almost like a hand. Some of these little fish that abound in tide pools but are usually unseen by the human eye are less than an inch long when *full grown*. They are the smallest vertebrates known. (A full grown, breeding adult goby, less than half an inch long, was discovered in a fresh-water pool in the Philippines by the renowned ichthyologist, Dr. Albert

Herre.) One needs sharp eyes to spot such creatures even after they have been poisoned and come falling out of their hiding places. As we spread the poison I cautioned Ensign Womeldorf to be on guard for even the smallest fish.

In a few minutes gasping, berserk fishes started coming to the surface. A tiny orange-spotted pufferfish blew up its white belly with air and looked like a floating golf ball. Ensign Womeldorf waded into the pool and scooped it into a hand net. "Is this a fish?" he asked with eyeballs like the puffer's belly.

We wore bathing suits and sneakers, and had face masks so that we could duck under and look around in the water. I warned Ensign Womeldorf and others who were now joining the spree, scooping stunned fishes from the surface with dip nets, not to touch any they didn't recognize because some might be poisonous. But they already knew this only too well.

It wasn't long before I saw a small brown fish that might easily have been mistaken for a part of the reef or a bit of seaweed lying loosely on the bottom of the pool. When I examined the creature, no longer than two inches, it was indeed a venomous scorpion fish. It had a series of erected hypodermic-like spines in its back fin, slight pressure on which could release poison from saclike glands near the base. Although the chances of accidentally stepping on such a fish are slight, it has been done and is one good reason for wearing sneakers in these areas.

In an hour we had dozens of fishes and we had used only eight ounces of the rotenone liquid. My worries had been needless and the success of our tide pool collecting surprised even me. We spread another ten ounces of the emulsion around as we could see a number of fish still unaffected. In another hour most of the fish in the pool had become specimens for science.

Our largest fish were over a foot long and included three species of sea bass (one of which was a beautiful dark brown with brilliant sky blue spots and supposed to be poisonous to eat), several kinds of whiskered goatfish, bronze-red squirrel fish, and a weird-looking trumpet fish with an elongated snout almost as long as his elongated body. It looked like Donald Duck slimmed to spaghetti-thin proportions. When we first saw this creature, it was moving like a long stick near the surface of the water with a current—except that there was no current in our tide pool! It was the first live (or at least half-live) trumpet fish that I had ever seen, and even though I knew what it was, I was as thrilled with it as Ensign Womeldorf who had never heard of such a creature.

We got a variety of lovely damsel fish including the black-striped *Abudefduf,* popularly called the convict fish or Sergeant Major because of its markings. We had a grand time catching gobies and blennies, those agile leapers that jumped out of our pool to escape its fouled water and went skipping over the dry reef to other, healthier tide pools, with several Naval officers hot on their trail.

Blennies and gobies are fascinating little fishes. Because of their ability to skip overland to reach other pools, they are quite difficult to catch. They not only fly through the air with the greatest of ease, but also with the greatest of speed. From a distance they look like little frogs leaping. And they don't scurry off willy-nilly. Even when they can't see over the hurdle they are about to jump, they usually land safely in a neighboring pool or open water. Do they know where they are going?

Dr. Lester Aronson, animal psychologist at the American Museum of Natural History, believes they do. By using some ingenious experimental procedures, Dr. Aronson made careful studies of the jumping behavior of gobies in the West Indies. He found that these fish are surprisingly well oriented in their jumps. He believes that during high tide, gobies swim over the tide pools and acquire an effective memory of the general features of the topography of a limited area around their home pool. And this memory gives them directional clues in emergency situations when locked in their pools at low tide.

Although we lost lots of gobies, the best jumpers of our Kwajalein tide pool were the blennies. Whatever system they used, it was effective.

The last fish to succumb to our poison were the eels, which varied from the pink and flesh-colored little worm eels to an assortment of small moray eels whose strikingly bold and beautiful color patterns lead many casual observers to believe them water snakes.

The sun was getting high in the sky and the tide coming in fast when we finally felt we had sufficiently combed the crevices and clumps of algae for all the dead fish. There were still a few darting about, full of life or just a little groggy but reviving with the influx of fresh ocean water.

Carrying our fish in buckets, we headed for the dispensary

where we stored them in a big icebox while we returned to our quarters to wash up and have lunch. After lunch we brought our specimens to the morgue where we sorted them and took a rough inventory. There were hundreds, including over sixty different kinds. The one-room morgue couldn't accommodate all the visitors who came to look over our catch. Some of the servicemen brought their cameras to take pictures. Ensign Womeldorf, squeamish at first about touching eels, obligingly posed with his hand in a bucketful of the elongated cadavers.

Our visitors asked many questions and seemed interested in learning the purpose of the tactile whiskers on a goatfish, the mechanics of the venomous spines of the scorpion fish, and the inflating mechanism of the belly of blowfishes. It made me wonder how less dull our boys would find their assignments on these islands if they knew more about the sea life surrounding them. Many stationed in the Pacific complain of how boring life became because they had "nothing to do" in their spare time. How few of them ever explored the reefs around these tropical islands! An inexpensive face mask or native-made goggles, bathing suit, and sneakers are all that are needed to see the coral reef world. What a thrill so many missed and how close they were to an endlessly absorbing pastime.

I made one bad mistake in this tide-pool collection. I neglected to have the formalin on hand when we first collected the fish. When picked out of water, they should have been dropped into the preserving fluid immediately. This would have prevented the slightest deterioration, made the specimens firm, and every spine and ray on the smallest fins (the number of which is of great importance in the final identification and study of the specimen) would have been distinct and in top condition. This collection, most of which is now in the U.S. National Museum, could be in better condition. Unfortunately, it was not until we started work in the morgue, and some of the specimens were developing a slimy coat, that I realized this neglect which I have avoided ever since.

Preparing and preserving the collection were a good afternoon's occupation. The boys were very helpful. We formed a sort of assembly line. Ensign Womeldorf on my right handed me a specimen which I examined, while another fellow, sitting on the opposite side of the table that ordinarily accommodates a cadaver, took down notes with his dry hands. I then handed the fish to a sailor on my left who, with a sharp knife, made a slit in the side of the belly of the larger fish so that the preserving fluid would reach the fast spoiling viscera. This sailor in turn handed the fish to a fourth assistant who placed it carefully in a proper-sized container with a ten per cent formalin solution.

The men co-operated enthusiastically in this procedure which apparently was a relieving break from their usual routine.

When our job for the day was nearly through, I was asked, "Did you find any new species?" For some reason this is the most popular question I am asked whenever I return from a collecting trip. Some time later, a *Life* magazine reporter even asked me what fish I expected to discover in the Red Sea *before* I had even gone there!

There is no doubt about it, the discovery of a new species is

an exciting experience for the discoverer. But it doesn't happen
the way some people imagine. It isn't very often that even an
expert ichthyologist sees a strange fish in his net and can an-
nounce, "Oh boy, a *new* species!" It happens of course on rare
occasions, but more often the story is like this:

Professor Doe (he may be one of the world's top ichthyologists; it happens to the best of them) looks in his collecting net
and thinks, "Here's a fish I'm not familiar with, maybe it's a
new species." He then takes color notes on the fresh specimen,
preserves it, and sets it aside. Later he carefully studies this fish,
measuring every proportion, counting all the little elements in
its fins, examining every inch of it, perhaps even dissecting it
to study its internal anatomy. Then he starts checking the literature to see if anything like it has ever been described before. He
goes through dozens of books and maybe hundreds of papers
published in five different languages. He consults colleagues.
Then a year or two or ten later he is finally convinced that this
fish is a new species. So he writes up all his notes, has a picture
made, baptizes his specimen, and publishes his results.

Often the story doesn't end here.

Some time later Professor Doe may find out by himself,
or through a letter, or worse still, he may read in print the
following revelation: That the supposedly new species of such
and such a fish described by Professor Doe was actually first
named by Dr. Bleeker. This reference can easily be found in an
antique set of volumes published in the Netherlands one
hundred years ago, today seldom found outside of museum
libraries. Dr. Bleeker found the fish in a different ocean about

ten thousand miles from where Professor Doe found his specimen, but it's the same species. Dr. Bleeker even published a
colored illustration of this fish. Unfortunately, his specimen was
slightly immature (a fact not known then) and so the colors
and body proportions are different—and one fin was partly
mutilated and so a few of its elements do not show in the
painting. But otherwise it's the same fish!

If Professor Doe is a young man, he may tear out a few
of his hairs; if he has had lots of experience he will probably
only sigh ... it is all part of his work. One man living in Tahiti,
who can't be bothered consulting all the literature on fishes, has
solved this problem for himself much to the dismay of
conscientious ichthyologists. When he can't identify a fish in
the few books he has on hand, he merely gives it a new name
and lets others worry about whether it is really new or not.
There are all kinds of ichthyologists!

In Kwajalein I visited Seaman Knight who was hospitalized
as the result of encountering a poisonous fish. Only the day
before I came to the island, he was looking in shallow water
and saw a small brown fish lying on a rock. It didn't move when
he went close to it and so he reached down to pick it up with
his hand. Then he felt a slight prick which made him release the
fish. In a few minutes the flesh around the prick started turning blue and three hours later his hand was swollen to the
wrist and his arm was numb. Ten hours after the prick he was
running a fever and the swelling had reached his shoulder.

I had brought along a handbook of Pacific fishes which had
an illustration of a scorpion fish. Seaman Knight said his fish

was very similar but flatter and had its mouth "topside." In spite of his short encounter with the venomous animal, he had made a good observation which narrowed down the identification of the fish to only a few of the forty-odd possible species known from the tropical Pacific. They range from the ugly toadfish to the beautifully delicate tigerfish. Seaman Knight's fish was probably the stonefish known to zoologists as *Synanceja verrucosa,* a name referring to the grooves in the dorsal spines through which the poison passes and to the warty condition of its skin.

Seaman Knight was actually lucky. His case could have been much worse. People have died from the sting of scorpion fish.

Most people, however, live to tell about their unpleasant meetings with scorpion fish. Few of these cases are recorded in full detail and the fish involved is seldom specifically identified. Recently, however, the renowned South African ichthyologist Dr. J. L. B. Smith, who last year discovered a "living fossil" coelacanthid fish supplied a firsthand account of a severe case of venomous fish poisoning where unfortunately he was the victim.

Dr. Smith was poisoning a tide pool on a collecting trip in Portuguese East Africa. Accidentally he was stabbed in the thumb by two dorsal spines of a stonefish which was still alive. He put a tourniquet around his thumb, made cuts across the punctures, and sucked these vigorously. His wife gave him novocaine but the pain became a "searing agony." Three and one half hours later the pain was undiminished. He tried immersing his hand in hot water and this gave him rapid relief. The flesh around the stabs turned black, large yellow blisters formed on his thumb, and swelling extended above the elbow. He developed an inflammation but treatment with penicillin, he believes, prevented serious secondary infection. After eighty days his thumb was still swollen and painful.

From a number of cases in the literature, it appears that the best treatment for venomous fish poisoning is similar to that

POISONOUS SCORPION FISH

for a snake bite. Perhaps someday antivenom for fish poison will also be developed.

Seaman Knight recovered in a week. His case was mild compared to Dr. Smith's, even though both were caused by a similar if not identical species of fish. If the stinging ability of the scorpion-type fishes is as effective on their natural enemies as it is on man, it is no wonder that a species of this sluggish group has survived successfully enough to range halfway around the world.

8

Guam: Whisky and Raw Fish

Guam was my next stop. It was a misty, hot, and humid morning when I arrived but the drive from the airport to the Naval base was along a scenic coastal road and there was a cool salty breeze. We passed some large Poinciana trees packed with red blossoms and looking like gaudy floral umbrellas from the float in a parade. Mile after mile went by and the picture in my mind of the dot on my map of the Pacific Ocean marked "Guam (U.S.A.)" grew to a large size.

The U.S. Trust Territory is composed of the Marianas, Marshall and Caroline island groups. But Guam, although one of the Marianas and the headquarters of the Trust Territory, is not actually part of the Trust Territory. Since 1898 Guam has been an outright possession of the United States (its natives are U.S. citizens) while the Trust Territory proper was acquired only after World War II. The Japanese had controlled these

Dr. Carl L. Hubbs, Professor of Ichthyology at the Scripps Institute of Oceanography, after extracting two octopi from crevices in tide pools near La Jolla. He is shown wearing a face mask and warm clothes sometimes used when underwater "goggling" during winter months.

The author on the E. W. Scripps, the research vessel of the Scripps Institute.

The author, standing besi[de] the diving helmet she used [in] the West Indies and holdi[ng] a sea fan. With her a[re] Clarence (*left*) and Ped[ro] (*right*), native assistants [at] the Lerner Marine Laborato[ry] on the island of Bimini.

A pair of courting guppies. The male's anal fin is extended forward and to the si[de] next to the female in a thrusting movement toward her genital region; the positi[on] just before copulation when the sperm is transferred to the female. Part of a stu[dy] made while the author worked in the Department of Animal Behavior at the Am[er]ican Museum of Natural History with Dr. Lester Aronson.

Siakong, a great spearfisherman of the Pacific Islands, who taught the author his art.

Right to left: Siakong (in his usual dress when not in the water), Niraibui, and an old fisherman in the one-cylinder boat used for trips to the outer reefs in the Palaus.

A native spearfisherman of So
sorol holding a poisonous tri
gerfish. He is wearing h
double-duty swim suit and fu
dress. The goggles are han
made, and so is the slingsh
type of spear, equipped with
broad band of rubber whi
sends the shaft through th
water.

An old woman weaving a basket
from a coconut tree frond on
the island of Merir.

Once stricken with polio, the wise and kindly monarch Ueg, King of Ulithi, travels everywhere around his island in his royal wagon.

The author sitting among the high chiefs of Fais, outside the *abai*.

A throw net hung up to dr[y]
in the village of Gekla[u]
Palau Islands.

The author with a throw net
in position for throwing.

Author demonstrating the method for opening a throw net—
at the American Museum of Natural History.

The author in one of her
first attempts to release a
throw net.

The author with face mask and wooden-handled spear that she used in the coral reefs of the South Seas.

Dr. Clark about to lower herself off the end of a boat anchored on a coral reef in the Red Sea. She is holding a speargun for shooting specimens. A wooden-handled harpoon (*right*) is kept ready for slower swimming fishes.

Dr. H. A. F. Gohar, Director of Egypt's Marine Biological Station, and the author with the poisonous but beautiful blue-spotted sting ray she had just speared underwater on a reef near Ghardaqa.

Parrot fish on spear.

Dr. Clark standing on a shallow ledge of corals in Sharks Bay just after spearing a porcupine fish or spiny blowfish. The fish is deflated as it was speared through its balloonlike stomach. This fish is thought to be poisonous to eat, but laboratory tests could find no poison in Red Sea samples of the species.

Atiyah, a native spearfisherman and the author with a morning catch.

The author examining the "mermaid" or dugong captured in the Red Sea at the Marine Biological Station at Ghardaqa.

The old head sailor with a dugong captured near the station in a shark net.

Dr. Gohar and Prince Ismail Hassan examining the 120 feet of alimentary tract from a dugong.

"Sea slugs" or nudibranch found on coral reefs in th Red Sea.

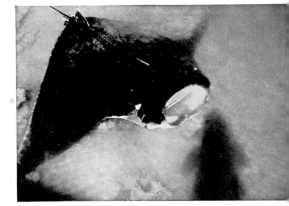

The giant manta ray that lived in the outdoor pool of the Station dwarfs the shadow of the photographer.

A native Arab woman an child.

Soliman the Sailor, the author, and Gomah.

Soliman holding a large skate or guitar fish, a relative of the shark group, common in the Red Sea.

Two types of small damsel fishes common among corals in shallow water. The plain fish is a brilliant emerald green (almost neon). The other is black and white striped. Both form large schools.

The author and native assistants collecting fishes after poisoning a tide pool on the Red Sea coast. Shehat, the houseboy with galabia skirt held in his teeth, also tried to help.

Mohammed, the versatile cook of the Marine Station, smoking his homemade pipe with a beer can built in to hold water. At right is his brother, Soliman the Sailor.

In long trips out to sea, the author and native fishermen took a large sailboat (*background*) and then used small dugout canoes to work in among the shallower reefs.

as standing in the Station's pool
th some large but harmless nurse
arks.

he Mako shark, one of the largest and most dangerous fishes found in the Red Sea.
This specimen was first captured alive and it gave birth to babies in the Station's pool.

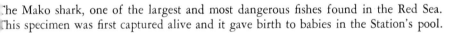

The remains of an ancient Roman quarry, hidden in the mountains of the Red Sea coast.

Gomah and the carpenter head for home hand in hand at the end of their day's work.

islands since the opening of World War I, before that the Germans, and still earlier they were controlled by Spain. Although most of the Trust Territory has much of the original charm we like to associate with South Sea Islands, relatively untouched by civilization, each nation that has taken over has left its mark and influenced the religion, language, social customs, and general living conditions of these once isolated natives.

I learned I would have to spend some time on Guam before proceeding to Koror. The officer in charge of accommodating official guests of the Navy on Koror had discovered that "E. Clark" was a woman and had hastily wired back to say I could not be put up at the Bachelor Officers' Quarters and there was no other place I could stay. Fortunately, however, I had been in contact with a young couple, Mr. and Mrs. Hill, who were in charge of a biological station just being organized on Koror. Mr. Hill wrote that they could put me up in about two weeks. I didn't mind waiting.

Guam was a new and fascinating place for me. I was given a room in a large, rather homey Quonset, where wives and children of Navy personnel were accommodated temporarily. The Naval base was situated on a high spot on the island called Commar Hill. The evenings here were cool and comfortable. That first evening I counted nearly a dozen geckos running across the outside of my big screen window, chasing the insects attracted by the light. When I was a child it was great fun to watch a few captured lizards in my terrarium; such an unusual sight for apartment dwellers that neighbors came to watch too. But on Guam every room with screen windows had a display of feeding lizards at night. These charming little geckos with large catlike eyes, long tails, and suction-padded toes—darting across the screen to capture insects on their sticky, elastic tongues—were as common a sight as houseflies back home. I liked my room. It had plenty of table space, I had all my fishing equipment with me, so I set myself up to do some work on Guam.

Where to eat my meals presented a technical problem. I didn't seem to fit in any of the categories into which the various mess halls were divided. I didn't mind where I ate, but there were regulations. . . . It was finally decided that I eat in the same building with the all-male officers, but in a special smaller room separated from the main dining room. I think I started a new category.

I ate alone at a long table, attractively arranged with fresh flowers, and set just for me. Two Guamanian waiters attended me ceremoniously while the rest of the kitchen help periodically peeked in through a little square glass window in the swinging door that led to the kitchen. The food was very good and there was no limit to the number of servings. Each morning I had a large glass of orange juice. Every sip I took from it was immediately replaced by a waiter standing by with a pitcher. When I left the table, no matter how much I drank, the glass was always full. It did no good to protest against these replacements; the glass would be filled the instant I could be taken unawares. When the smiling waiter was not filling my glass, he was shooing the flies away from me, scolding them in his broken English as if they were not Guamanian flies.

The other waiter brought in the food. Each time he presented me with a dish, he asked beaming, "You like?" Nothing seemed to please him more than when I asked for a second helping. Instead of being lonely eating by myself, I began to enjoy the luxury of what I was coming to regard as my private dining room.

The people on Guam were good to me and very helpful. Mr. Joyce Taggert, or "Tag" as everyone called him, gave me much information about the Fisheries work in the Trust Territory. He was the Fisheries advisor in that area. Although he hastened to tell me he was not a "scientific man," he had an enormous store of practical knowledge about fishes, where they are found, which are poisonous, and native fishing customs. "How long have you been out in the Pacific?" I asked him.

"Since long before you were born," he told me laughing, then showed an old, browning photograph of a rugged, windswept-looking man standing on a sailboat. There was a slight resemblance to Tag. "That's me years ago when I was a pirate in Tahiti," he said with such a wild gleam in his eye that I almost believed him. Later I met his wife. She was the type who could turn a carefree "sea pirate" willingly into a Fisheries consultant for the Navy. They had a blonde young daughter who had been born in the Palaus. She spoke fluent Palauan to her nursemaid who had taken care of her since she was a baby. The Taggerts gave me the first detailed description of the Palaus. They had lived on the main island, Koror, for years and loved the place.

While waiting to go to Koror I made seven fish collections on Guam. The first pools I poisoned were at the bottom **of**

Commar Hill where I was staying. In a series of four small tide pools I obtained over two hundred specimens many of which were very different from those we got at Kwajalein. Another time some officers were driving to Umatac, a native village on the other side of the island. They offered to take me along and help poison a tide pool on the way. We made a small but interesting collection of the young stages of several trigger-fishes, along with thirty other species of fishes, all in shallow pools less than a foot deep.

Umatac was a village where children rode around the streets on the backs of large water buffaloes. It was a long drive around Guam to reach Umatac which gave me a chance to see more of the island. There was a lush growth of coconut trees on this part of the island in contrast to the straggly growth around Commar Hill where the coconut beetles had done almost as much as World War II to destroy the tropical beauty of that now densely populated part of Guam.

A few days later I went to a place called Ylig Bay. I heard that a fresh-water stream ran into it and I was hoping to find a place narrow enough to get a sample of fishes that might be living in the brackish water. But I was out of luck. The stream was wide and deep and even where it joined the bay I could find no partly enclosed places which had any fish in them.

Further out in the bay I saw a large fish trap. It had long wire fencing leading to the entrance of the trap from three directions over an angle of about 140°. A fisherman with water goggles on his head and carrying a spear and basket, was wading out toward the trap. I called out to him and asked if I

could look in the trap too. I put on my face mask and swam
over to him. He spoke no English but led me to believe by
his gestures that although he didn't expect much in the trap
I could come along if I wanted to.

The trap was about two hundred yards from shore but the
water there came only to my shoulders. The fisherman adjusted
his goggles over his eyes and ducked underwater. I pulled my
glass mask down in place on my face (I keep it perched on
my head like a pillbox-type hat when not looking underwater)
and followed the fisherman. The water wasn't too clear and
in addition we had stirred up the sandy bottom with our feet.

The main portion of the trap was box shaped, almost square,
about four feet in each dimension. The frame was made of
bamboo and the sides with chicken wire fencing. On one side,
the wire was open and curved inward like a funnel so that the
sharp edges of the wire pointed toward the center of the trap
—a typical trapping device that permits the animal to squeeze
in easily but not out. This was the innermost chamber of the
trap. There was a larger chamber about three feet wide and
thirty feet long just outside the entrance to the inner box-
shaped chamber. The opening to the larger chamber connected
with the three long radiating fences which apparently steered
the fish toward the center as the tide went out.

That day there were few fish in the trap as the man had pre-
dicted. But his small catch was of much interest to me. It
consisted of seven good-sized poisonous pufferfish. I pointed to
them enthusiastically but the fisherman shook his head, made a
motion of eating, then held his stomach, and made painful

grimaces. He wanted to throw the fish away but I kept telling him I wanted them. Finally he consented to let me have them, but warned me over and over with his pantomiming not to eat them.

Back in my room at Commar Hill, I prepared samples of these fish to send to some investigators at the Hooper Foundation in San Francisco for laboratory analyses. They were willing to test all the samples I could send them of fish suspected of being poisonous to eat.

Fish that are poisonous to eat present a very different kind of problem from the venomous varieties, like scorpion fish, where the danger lies in contact. Venomous fishes can usually be eaten with impunity if the limited areas where the poison is known to be concentrated are avoided. The barbed spines on the whip-like tails of sting rays are cut off after capture and the rest of the fish used as food in many parts of the world. Scorpion fish are often sold in some Mediterranean fish markets. The types of venomous fishes are few and fairly easy to recognize. The same species are poisonous wherever they are found. Not so with fish that are poisonous to eat.

The same fish is sometimes poisonous to eat, and sometimes not. Certain barracuda are believed to be poisonous only after they reach a certain size. Other species are said to be poisonous only at a certain season and in certain localities. In some fishes the poison is all over, in others it is found only in certain organs. Sometimes the natives in one locality will not agree on the toxicity of a certain fish: some will claim it is highly poisonous while others will eat it readily. The manner in which the fish is prepared may have much to do with its edibility. Various authorities list anywhere from one hundred to over three hundred poisonous-to-eat species of fish in the Pacific. Many of these so closely resemble wholesome food fishes that it takes an expert to tell them apart.

Dr. Yoshi Hiyama, a Japanese ichthyologist who surveyed this problem in the 1930's, made one general conclusion. Most poisonous-to-eat fishes are found in tropical waters near coral reef formations. He suggested there might be a correlation between poisonous fishes and corals. Other investigators also tend to think that something in the environment, probably something the fish feeds on, can produce the poison in its body.

The illness that comes from eating a poisonous fish has been termed "ichthyotoxism." It should not be confused with the ptomaine type of poisoning that results from eating spoiled fish. Any fish may become unfit to eat when bacterial decay sets in; but with fishes that have a definite toxin to begin with, no assurance of freshness can prevent a case of poisoning.

Dr. Halstead, who has reviewed the reports of fish poisoning, finds the symptoms of ichthyotoxism quite characteristic. Some of the symptoms are so unusual that the general clinical picture of ichthyotoxism is easy to tell from other types of poisoning. The reactions can be extremely unpleasant and result in death. Within thirty hours after eating a poisonous fish, there is a tingling of the lips and tongue which spreads to the hands and feet and gradually develops into a numbness. In most cases stomach and intestinal disturbances appear such as nausea, vomiting, diarrhea, and abdominal pain. These may be followed by disturbances of the nervous system and the victim becomes irritable, convulsive, or paralyzed. Throat spasms may cause choking. There may be joint aches, chills, fever, profuse sweating, itching, temporary blindness, painful urination, and a metallic taste in the mouth. Perhaps the most unusual symptoms are certain erroneous sensations such as the reverse-temperature sensation and the "loose-tooth" sensation causing victims to blow on ice cream to cool it or complain that their teeth are falling out.

The poison itself is a fairly heat-stable alkaloid. Thus long cooking does not reduce the toxicity although leaching the flesh in salt water may remove some of it. Some Japanese investigators claim to have crystallized the pure toxin. Japan and the United States are the two main countries actively engaged in ichthyotoxism research. We hope their combined efforts in the next few years will solve the major problems of fish poisoning.

The most successful native fisherman on Guam was said to be Mr. Quenga. He had something of a monopoly on the trap fishing area just north of Sleeping Camel Rock. Arrangements were made for me to spend a day trap fishing in this area with the Quengas.

Mr. Quenga's son, Ramon, came to call for me in the morning, and much to my surprise, escorted me to the fishing wharf in a most elegant, large, new Buick. At the wharf our mode of transportation went back a few centuries and we shifted our fishing equipment into a primitive wooden outrigger canoe.

Ramon's uncle joined us in this and we paddled off toward the sea.

In the course of the day we examined seven large traps of the same type as the one I saw at Ylig Bay but every one of these yielded from a dozen to over a hundred good food fish. Ramon's uncle seemed to have come along just for the ride. He spoke no English and seemed to eye me suspiciously. He sat quietly in the canoe while Ramon and I did the paddling.

When we reached a trap, Ramon and I put on our underwater goggles and slipped beneath the rippled surface of the water down into shallow clear water. It was usually about five feet deep around the traps. First we swam along the wire fencing and Ramon pointed out the prized food fishes and other unusual specimens that were caught inside the trap—especially all the plectognath fishes which he knew I wanted to see.

What an assortment of colorful reef fishes was in each trap! There were many green parrot fish, red squirrel fish, spotted groupers, snappers, surgeon fish, butterfly fish and several kinds of trigger- and blowfish. We got dozens of delicious eating crabs, lobsters, and squid. We would chase the animals to one corner of the trap where Ramon scooped them out with a large dip net and piled them into the canoe. One trap had a three-foot shark in it which Ramon neatly speared through the head before attempting to capture it.

Between traps, when we paddled over an attractive reef, Ramon and I slipped over the side of the canoe and looked at its inhabitants through our water goggles. Ramon spoke English fairly well. He was learning it at school. Although he was only sixteen years old, he was an experienced fisherman and was very helpful in answering my questions about his trade. As the oldest boy in a family of eight children, he had a number of responsibilities, the leading one being to check his father's traps every two or three days.

Near noon our silent watchman spoke to Ramon. "He wants to eat some lunch," Ramon informed me. We were some distance from shore and had not finished with all the traps yet. I hadn't thought to bring any lunch. Ramon's uncle produced a small bag which apparently contained all he ever brought along for his sea picnic: a lemon, an empty glass tumbler, and a large bottle of some kind of liquid.

The man then pulled out a knife, swiftly degutted a half-live squid, and then looking at me as if to be sure I was watching, he bit off a big chunk of the squid's mantle. As he chewed this mouthful, a devilish gleam came to his eyes and he suddenly passed the slimy decapod to me. He spoke Guamanian but I understood he was urging me to join him in this dish. As I stared at the squid in my hands, its tentacles hanging down between my fingers and its large greenish eyes staring back at me, the man broke into a roar, rocking back and forth in his place until I thought he would fall out of the canoe. Through this almost hysterical laughter he gasped some remarks to Ramon. Ramon looked embarrassed, glanced at me sheepishly, and then said something to his uncle which seemed to be the Guamanian equivalent of, "Aw, unk, you shouldn't have done that!"

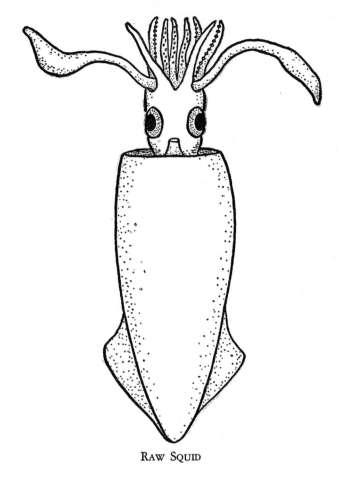

RAW SQUID

The old man only laughed harder and the half chewed pieces of squid nearly flew out of his mouth. He finally calmed down, though still breathing heavily, and looked at me with smiling though kind eyes.

I had eaten raw oysters, clams, and fish, and I was very fond of *cooked* squid and octopi the way my stepfather prepares them in cucumber salad—but a raw squid was something new for me. However, I have always liked to try new dishes and certainly the raw limp squid I held could taste no worse than gulping down an oyster whose heart still beats while it slides down your gullet. I decided to have a try at it, took a bite, and found it wasn't half bad. Ramon's uncle let out a cry and lifted his eyebrows in an expression of mingled shock and pleasure. From then on we were friends. Ramon didn't eat any of the squid but between his uncle and me it was finished off.

Ramon's uncle then skinned a large brown surgeon fish with two bright orange "knives" on each side of the base of its tail. It had been caught in the last trap we examined. The old man washed the cleaned fish in sea water, squeezed a little lemon over the cool firm flesh, and we three ate it with gusto. In the Pacific I learned that raw fish and other sea foods can be eaten in fairly large quantities and yet they are light in the stomach and do not cause discomfort or cramps even though followed immediately by hours of underwater swimming or similar heavy exercise. Also this type of food quenches the thirst as the flesh of raw fish contains fresh water.

As we concluded our sea picnic, Ramon's uncle filled his glass tumbler with an amber fluid from the large bottle in his lunch bag and handed it directly to me. As I took my first and only sip a sharp odor hit my nose. I couldn't hide a shudder and my general reaction of disapproval, much to the surprise of Ramon's uncle. It was undoubtedly fine whisky but one of those things I don't care for, especially with a noonday sun above and a rocking canoe below.

"Never mind," the elder Quenga seemed to gesture to me and then through Ramon's translation he told me he would bring a Coca-Cola for me the next time.

The rest of the trip went by too quickly. We emptied the remaining traps, chatted about the various animals we caught, poisonous fishes, fishing methods, etc. Ramon and his uncle chanted an odd little tune I couldn't understand, as we paddled toward shore.

At the wharf we unloaded what Ramon told me was an exceptionally large catch of fish. A number of Guamanians gathered around. Ramon's uncle introduced me to some of them and from his motions I gathered he was telling them that I had joined him in eating the raw squid. From the way they smiled with wrinkled noses (and remembering Ramon's abstinence), I suspect that raw squid may be enjoyed by only a few and probably is not a regular Guamanian dish.

After piling all our fish in the back of the Buick, we drove to Ramon's house, where his father greeted me warmly and bade me be his guest for supper.

Two crude weighing machines hung at the side of his house. Most of the fish were sorted, weighed, and sold on the spot to a group of waiting natives who paid almost a dollar a pound for the best quality fish and walked off contentedly with their purchases wrapped in newspaper. Ramon's father did a good business.

The Buick was not Mr. Quenga's only car, either. He proudly showed me two other equally new-looking cars in the back of his large but rather ramshackle house. Then he led me into a spacious but decrepit dirt-floor kitchen which had only three walls. The fourth, broken away, formed a short cut for the chickens, dogs, and cats to roam in and out of the house. The cooking was done on a crude open hearth but an ample supply of Cokes was kept in a huge, modern refrigerator which the average American housewife would envy. And they had a washing machine!

Papa Quenga was pleased with the fish we had brought back. But his spirits were particularly high that day because a two-hundred-dollar bet he had made on a cockfight had just paid off and the pockets of his baggy trousers were bulging with carelessly stuffed-in bills.

We can't brag about our "Southern hospitality" to Guamanians. If Quenga's family was representative of Guamanians, they can't be beat when it comes to all-out entertaining of a guest.

If you didn't care to start off with a glass of straight whisky, you could have all the Cokes or fresh coconut milk you desired while the food was brought to the table by a parade of Quenga's children. First we had scrambled fresh eggs—a real treat for Americans stationed on Guam at that time when powdered eggs were practically the only kind you could get. The delicious eggs were followed by roast chicken, lobsters, crabs, and freshly baked bread. It was truly a feast and my host beamed as he watched me enjoy it.

After we finished eating, Mr. Quenga showed me the rest of his house, including a special room with his large collection of shells. He tried to give me every shell I admired and finally insisted that I at least take his most flawless shell of a chambered nautilus.

I asked to meet Quenga's wife, for Ramon had mentioned his mother. I was led to a room upstairs. Quenga knocked on a door, "Mama, come meet American fish lady." Soon the door opened halfway and a woman, obviously in agony, thrust her hand out and shook mine while trying to smile weakly. Quenga motioned her back into the room and closed the door. "I like to have boy for fisherman," he smiled hopefully as I realized with a shock that his wife was in the process of having a baby!

When I left, Quenga gave me a large bag of fresh eggs and five large food fishes for my friends on Commar Hill, in addition to all the plectognaths we had gotten that day. He waved me off with a sparkling smile and shouted, "Remember Quenga!" as Ramon started the Buick that drove me back to my lodgings.

9

Saipan and Tide-pool Treasures

It is less than an hour by plane from Guam to Saipan. On the way one passes over the smaller islands of Rota and Tinian. These four islands form the southern extreme of a chain that, on a map of the Pacific, looks like stepping stones from the South Seas to Japan. Saipan is an exquisite island; smaller than Guam which makes it easier to get around, and yet large enough to be inexhaustibly interesting. I had time to arrange a trip to Saipan, where I was invited to stay with the family of Commander Sheffield, the Governor of the Marianas. An alcove of the back porch was fixed with a spacious work table and bookshelves where I could sort and study my specimens.

The Sheffields came on a few of my collecting trips and we combined scientific research with picnics. In the evenings they liked to help me sort the fishes and make notes. The carefully handwritten labels of Dolly, the Sheffields' young daughter, are still on some of my specimens.

We had grand times together on the beach outside their house. We'd watch the sun set and try to catch the "green flash" as the last of the red ball disappeared into the ocean—while pork chops cooked on an open grill next to us. When the moon came out we went swimming.

The Sheffields had a way of enjoying themselves with the abandon of children at play. One night we went on a sand crab hunt, running up and down the beach with flashlights and nets, shouting and laughing at our victories over the side-runners. Some of the crabs scurried into the water and we splashed after them in vain, just for the fun of wetting our feet. Once the crab reached the sea, he soon burrowed into the soft sand and left no trace behind. As soon as we had enough, we boiled our catch and had a delicious crab feast, amiably wrangling about whose crabs tasted best as we nibbled and sucked each last little shell-covered leg so as not to miss any of the tender meat inside.

The Sheffields had a most fascinating pet—though they assured me not all their guests thought so. Some months earlier, a large female fruit bat had been shot. When the fallen carcass was examined a little baby was found clinging to it. Mrs. Sheffield took it home and raised it on milk, oranges, and most of the vegetable and fruit dishes that were part of the regular family meals. The little brown creature thrived well and soon grew until it had a wing spread of over two feet. It was a dark blackish brown, and when it hung fairly motionless (as it often did) on a lamp, side table, or back of a wooden frame chair, it so blended with the furniture that visitors wouldn't notice it at first. But it was a curious bat. If you stood or sat near it, it

would look you over carefully, wiggling its ears at every sound
you made, and then quietly and carefully, it would stretch out
a wing to feel you. If you offered no resistance, you would soon
find the fellow hanging upside down from your shoulder and
looking up into your face. More often, however, visitors were
startled to say the least and in the midst of shudders and
screams, the bat would fly off to another part of the house, banking expertly in the turns of the dark hallways, and emitting
shrill squeaks. But to the Sheffields it was indeed a pet, and Mrs.
Sheffield especially fondled and played with it as you would
with a poodle.

Tag came to Saipan for a few days. He showed me the best
reefs for collecting fish by poisoning—a series of shallow inter-
connecting coralline pools on a fringing reef off Magpi Point
on the northwest side of Saipan. In all the rest of my tide-pool
collecting in the Pacific, I never found such an ideal spot. Pools
less than two feet deep were crowded with coral growths that
harbored thousands of fishes. One pool was the haven for no
less than fifty-seven different kinds of fishes! There were many
more kinds of invertebrate animals. We avoided the prickly
sea urchins, whose spines could pierce the sides of our sneakers
if we weren't watchful. And we played with the baby octopi
that came crawling out of their rotenone-penetrated crevices,
blushing when they saw us and squirting little black clouds in
the water when we touched them. But these we left unharmed.
It was only the fish that we dropped unmercifully into our con-
tainers of formalin.

Among the larger eels that wriggled out of the corals were conger eels and morays. The conger eels were all of one uniform gray species, and the more pleasant looking of the two types. They had characteristically prominent pectoral fins which, in a head-on view, looked like protruding ears. We got several species of the practically finless, ferocious-looking moray eels. One kind, with a brown-and-white mottled scaleless skin, Tag identified as a species that is good eating in the Philippines but which proved a deadly meal for some Filipinos who recently ate the Saipan specimens. I prepared samples of this eel to send to the Hooper Foundation for analysis.

Of our large variety of colorful reef fish, the most fascinating were two plectognaths. They were so irresistibly charming I knew Dolly would squeal with delight when she saw them later. If only they could keep their colors until then!

One of these was a baby boxfish. If his length of a mere two inches seemed insignificant, he made up for it with his gaudy color and comical figure. He was a brilliant orange with large black polka dots. He looked as if he had been upholstered in a strip of cloth from the dress of a Ringling Brothers' clown. He had immense dark, shining eyes and an absurdly tiny, round mouth—his face looked like a Betty Boop caricature. He was wiggling through the water like a polliwog. When Tag picked up his little boxlike body, he blew bubbles out of his miniature mouth and slapped his fanlike tail from side to side. His tail was one of the few movable parts of his otherwise rigid body. If one could keep this little fellow in a home aquarium along with guppies and angelfish, what an amusing pet he would be!

Some boxfish, of course, are displayed in salt-water aquaria but I had never seen one as cute as this. And yet—into the formalin he had to go. Even to this day, lifeless and colorless in a glass jar on the museum shelf, he can attract your eye with his funny little body and big, ever-open eyes.

Although there is hardly any superficial resemblance between boxfish and filefish, they belong to related families in the order of plectognath fishes. The filefish are known technically as "monacanthids" which in Greek refers to the prominent single spine on the back of a filefish and has also given rise to its popular English name.

Living in the same pool with our Betty Boop boxfish was a species of filefish that could only come from the underwater fairyland one finds in tropical coral reefs. It was a golden-spotted, emerald fish, the minutest of the monacanthids, a toy-like jewel which could be a model for the most exquisite of scatter pins—if one could capture its living colors. It wore bright yellow lipstick around a little mouth situated at the end of an elongated, tubelike snout. The eyes had remarkable irises: twelve radiating spokes of blue and orange. When we picked one up, little grinding sounds vibrated within its body; it fluttered its delicate, transparent fins in rippling movements, stretched its tail into a tense fan, erected its long, sharp, dorsal spine, and lowered a little flap from its belly. Although less than two inches long, the females of these filefish were mature and "ripe." A light squeeze of their abdomens and hundreds of translucent, sparkling, emerald eggs oozed out like tiny beads of mint jelly. Male and female seem exactly alike, but it was then that I noticed a way to tell the difference between them without having to squeeze for the evidence. Close examination of the small abdominal flap just before the anal opening revealed the clue to the sexes. Following one of the most general rules concerning the coloration of vertebrates (excluding people—they wear artificial makeup and don't count), which is that the male is usually the more ornate and colorful, the male filefish's abdominal flap was the more brilliant. When the flap was pale yellow, pressure above it brought forth the stream of green eggs; when the flap was bright orange topped with a white-spotted black area, a similar pressure brought forth the milky drops of sperm.

It was a wrench to leave Saipan. So little is known about the fishes around this island that I could have spent my whole time there profitably. But I had no choice. Other plans, other waters were waiting to be explored.

10

The Palaus and the Best Spearfisherman

I was permitted to look through the wide front windshield, over the pilot's shoulder, as our "tramp steamer of the airways" approached the Palauan Islands. An intricate mass of hundreds of green pieces of land lay scattered ahead. I couldn't figure out which was Koror.

Our seaplane docked at what they said was Arakabesan, an island next to Koror. I could see a group of people watching us from shore. A blonde head stood out among them, reflecting the sun almost like a mirror. As we disembarked I found it belonged to an attractive and charming young lady who thrust a bouquet of gardenias into my hands. "Welcome to the Palaus!" she greeted me warmly. With her was a tall, lanky fellow with glasses and sharp features. These were the Hills, newlyweds from Michigan, who were in charge of the Pacific War Memorial Station on Koror where I was supposed to make my headquarters for the rest of my stay in the Pacific.

"I warned you in my letters not to expect anything fancy," Peter Hill emphasized as we drove up to a two-story building in a bomb-blasted area. "This used to be a Japanese weather station. The Navy still uses the upstairs as such—you'll notice a balloon going up every night. We live in one half of the ground floor, the other half is being made into a lab. Actually, we're far from ready to accommodate visiting scientists."

In the next few weeks several other SIM scientists passed through the Palaus: a zoology professor from Swarthmore who was studying the types and distribution of Pacific rats; a young orchid specialist and an elderly sponge expert from the University of Hawaii; a malacologist from the Bishop Museum who was studying a control measure for the fiercely spreading African land snail that the Japanese had introduced. Each came to the Station expecting nothing fancy but just some little haven where he could sort his collection and camp and chat with fellow field collectors. We were all prepared to "rough it"—in fact that is part of the fun of field work. As it turned out, the sponge expert and I shared a half-built but comfortable Quonset hut belonging to the Memorial Station and the rest lived at the Navy BOQ.

I was permitted to eat at the BOQ, but as it was some five miles away and I had no regular means of transportation I took to eating at a little native restaurant, less than two miles away, that served Palauan and Japanese food. The proprietress always joined me when she saw I was eating alone. She spoke no English but she made an effort to understand my attempts at Japanese and would try to teach me some Palauan. The latter was very hard for me to grasp. As most Palauans speak Japanese, I thought it best to struggle with that language during my few months' stay here.

Most of the Navy personnel on Koror were not exactly fond of visiting scientists. They didn't like to be disturbed by a group of eccentrics out collecting fish, rats, snails, orchids, and sponges. Fortunately most of my dealings were with the always kind and helpful natives and the few members of the Navy who were more tolerant. Lt. Harry Stille, who handled native affairs,

OUTRIGGER CANOE

and Harry Uyehara, a Japanese-Hawaiian who worked mainly as an interpreter, were a great help to me from the beginning. They took me to a native "Congress" meeting, explaining to the Congress that I was making a study of poisonous fishes. I was introduced to the magistrates and chieftains of most of the native districts in the Palaus. While Harry interpreted, the native leaders told me about the types of poisonous fishes in the local waters, where I might find them, and which fishermen I might rely on for more help. And so I started making contacts with the natives.

The Palauan people have an odd mixture of native and adopted names. The first two fishermen who took me trap fishing were Ngiraibuuch and Milimara. There was a native called Stanislaus who helped me poison pools with my rotenone preparation. He also tried to poison himself by eating the ripe eggs of a blowfish when his wife left him. And there was Bismark who showed me how to use the fresh roots of the local Derris plant to poison fish in open reef waters. But the name Siakong recalls the most wonderful underwater adventures I experienced in the South Seas.

Siakong was a betel-chewing, wife-beating drunkard. But he was the best spearfisherman in the Palaus—or maybe in the whole world, I sometimes think now. I'm not just biased because he taught me spearfishing and one hundred other things about the underwater world. His stupendous skill was an undisputed fact among all the Palauans.

Siakong was just over fifty when I knew him. What he was like in his youth will be a legend of the Palaus. The stories about him are unbelievable—probably exaggerated by the tellers, including Siakong himself. But I will tell you what facts I know about him—my firsthand experiences with him in the waters around the Palaus.

Siakong worked for the Hills. He was their most valuable general handy man for he could do the work that required the physical strength of three average Palauans. Although Siakong had been recommended to me as the best fisherman I could find, and I had but a few precious weeks to spend in those islands, Peter Hill would not allow me to borrow Siakong during working hours. Fortunately the work day ended at 3 P.M. and so I could hire him to come with me on late afternoon trips and all day Sunday.

Siakong knew a native, Niraibui, who owned a one-cylinder inboard motorboat that could hold up to six people. So besides the three of us we sometimes took other fishermen and on Sundays we'd invite Harry Uyehara and one or two of the SIM scientists who happened to be there that week. The professor from Swarthmore was as impressed by Siakong's magnificent build and strength as the rest of us and promptly nicknamed him King Kong.

A small red loincloth and homemade goggles formed Siakong's diving outfit. The rest of the time he wore an old pair of khaki shorts over his loincloth, a dirty handkerchief tied around his head and a decrepit straw hat over the handkerchief. When he took these off to go into the water he was suddenly metamorphosed from a bum into a Greek God.

Siakong knew the best places to get the plectognaths I was after and these seemed to be where there were the most beautiful coral reefs. These reefs were a long way out from the town of Koror. We usually went there via Malakal Harbor where we could look deep down into the clear water and see sunken battleships from the war days. Niraibui's motor conked out every so often and sometimes we found ourselves paddling back so late that the water was inky black, except where our paddles made a trail of phosphorescence given off by the microorganisms we disturbed.

Siakong had an exceptionally nice lightweight throw net which he had made himself out of nylon. Even I learned to use this net a little. I had no luck at all with the heavy, bulky cotton throw nets of other fishermen. Siakong's spears, however, were his main equipment. They had metal heads and bamboo handles and were deftly balanced so that you could maneuver them underwater with ease, regardless of their length. Some of them were over twelve feet. And they were just light enough for the bamboo end to float so you could recover them easily. He also had several shorter-handled, four-pronged spears for catching small fish. The prongs on these were small and fine and Siakong could get me a tiny filefish without perceptibly damaging it.

It was great fun to watch Siakong spear fish from above the water. He would stand on the bow of Niraibui's boat as we putt-putted to the outer reefs, a long spear in each hand. I would sometimes stand up searching the water too but I could never spot a fish before Siakong did. A spear was flying through the air as I opened my mouth to call out, "There's a fish!" If the first spear missed, the second one was on its way in a flash and Siakong seemed to predict the direction in which the fish would dodge the first spear. Whether he got the fish or not this was a noisy affair once the spears were thrown, for Siakong would be either cheering or cursing himself at the top of his lungs.

Underwater it was different. He never made a sound but I could see him grinning broadly and his eyes sparkled through

his water goggles. Here, there was no suspense about whether
or not Siakong would get the fish he was after. It was only a
question of how long it would take him and by what trick he
would get it.

The first fish I speared was a triggerfish. But it never made
a specimen for a museum. It was a beauty about nine inches
long of pastel orange and yellow and with a large, black spot
in the middle of its body. I'd never seen this species before although I had read about it. I chased it with no more finesse
than a child reaching for an ice-cream cone. When I managed
to get above it and made ready to lunge with my spear, it
turned on its side to give me a last good look and then slipped
into a small hole in the reef. But its tail end was still half out.
What a cinch, I thought to myself. It was like spearing a sta-
tionary object. The first thrust of the spear didn't penetrate the
tough skin but the second did. "Got you!" I muttered triumphantly to myself.

Then I tried to pull the fish up by the spear but it was stuck
tight in the hole. I pulled and pulled but only succeeded in
pulling out my spear and leaving a big gash in my specimen. I
speared it again and pulled with the same result. I stuck the
spearhead into the hole and then into the front end of the triggerfish. Still no luck. By this time I had done a fine job of
tearing my specimen to shreds, but its head was still tightly
fixed in the hole. I gave up and joined Siakong, who was spearing fish some distance away.

A large brown triggerfish swam within sight of us. I pointed
to it but Siakong was already slowly swimming after it, circling

around it to head it off from going into deep water. Finally it went into a hole—but again the rear end was sticking out.

Then Siakong did something I thought was odd. He let his spear float to the surface and he dove after the fish empty-handed. Siakong went right to the hole and, gripping a piece of heavy coral with his left hand, he slipped his right hand into the hole with the fish. He looked up at me with a triumphant grin as he withdrew the fish with his hand.

Then it dawned on me what he had done. Triggerfish are so named because of an ingenious mechanism in their first dorsal fin. This fin has three spines, the first of which is large and tough. When swimming around, triggerfish usually keep this fin folded flat on their backs. When frightened, however, a triggerfish will often slip into a small opening and then erect its large spine, thus locking itself in its hiding place. No amount of pushing or pulling can lower this spine and it is very hard to break.

But the third spine on that same fin, although sometimes so small it shows as nothing more than a tiny button, is actually the *releaser* for the first spine. A slight pressure on it and the whole fin collapses. Siakong of course knew this trick and had simply pushed the right button to back the fish out of its hole!

It wasn't always quite so simple, however. Sometimes a triggerfish would go deep into a crevice in the coral until it was out of sight and a hand could not reach the release spine on the fin. For this situation Siakong had a chisel and with the help of a stone, he'd break away the coral around the hiding fish. It wasn't easy for a fish to escape Siakong.

Once I pointed out a fish to him it was as good as mine. He was a keen observer and his years of underwater experience made him an expert fish psychologist. He knew the ways of every one of the hundreds of varieties of reef fishes. He didn't always go directly after a fish but would watch it a few seconds, calculate its next move, and then head it off into a place where it could easily be caught.

One of Siakong's methods of spearing fish underwater was literally breath taking, as well as remarkably simple. He would find a reef well populated with fish and then dive calmly to about ten or twenty feet, sometimes weighting himself with a rock so he could sink without swimming. He'd get a firm grip on the reef with his legs or his free arm, poise his spear in readiness and then *wait* for the fish to come to him!

The first time I watched him do this it alarmed me. He dived and lay motionless on the reef, like an animal about to spring on its prey. His brown body and red loin cloth blended in with the kaleidoscope of colors on the surrounding reef. The fish began to regard him as part of the corals and came very close.

I was watching from above. Not used to Siakong's extraordinary lung capacity, I began to worry after a long time passed and he didn't move. So I swam down to him and tapped him on the head to make sure he was all right. He turned and looked up at me with his usual underwater grin as I reached for a piece of coral to hold myself down. I tried to make a gesture with my face to ask him what he was doing but he was looking at my hand and the grin had dropped from his face. He reached for my arm as I felt the "coral" under my hand suddenly move.

I was holding onto the side of a giant "man-eating" clam. The clam had just snapped shut and my fingers were only a fraction of an inch from the opening between the two halves of the shell. These close with a viselike grip that can hold a diver's arm or leg until he drowns.

As we swam up to the surface, Siakong pointed to the wall of coral along which I had carelessly descended. Partly imbedded in the corals were dozens of these clams, all with their shells gaping open. The shells looked like gray dead corals. Inside, the soft flesh had the beautiful colors of the surrounding living corals and the plants and animals that encrust them. Some were iridescent green, others blue, purple, and shades of brown mingled with irregular darker patches. They were well camouflaged but from then on I learned to distinguish them from anything else.

Siakong taught me, however, that even the largest of these clams can be handled safely and that they are among the most delicious of raw sea foods. He would dive down to an open clam and wave his hand over it. Often this was enough to stimulate the light-sensitive flesh inside and the clam would close. If not, he tapped the side of the shell. Then he pried the clam loose and brought it up with him. With a rock or his chisel he chipped open a part of the curved meeting edges of the shell—just enough to slip in the blade of his knife. Then a little cut in just the right place and the shell would fall right open and we could reach in and pull out all the "meat."

Almost every part of the giant clam can be eaten raw though actually I think the soft reproductive organs and tough colored parts are better cooked. But the adductor muscle—the large white muscle that connects the two halves of the shell and closes the clam with such force—is truly a gourmet's delight. I have never tasted anything more delicious. It need only be washed off in sea water and it is ready for eating. It has a texture that is like biting into a crisp cucumber. It has a sweet, clean, indescribably pleasant flavor. From the first time I tried it, the raw adductor muscle of the giant clam has been my favorite sea food. It became a regular part of our reef picnics along with raw fish, a tasty pinkish seaweed that grew in spaghettilike strands, and tiny limpets.

Limpets are distant relatives of snails but with low conical shells that resemble the hats of Chinese coolies. The species we ate clung to the rocks near the water line by the thousands in some places. A twist of a small knife would free the flesh (sometimes no more than the size of a pea) from the shell. The first time we came across them, Niraibui and I sat in the boat eating them by the dozens as fast as a grinning Siakong could pick them off the rocks. We never had to bring any lunches with us, for we were always swimming among more good sea food than we could ever eat. Sometimes, if the day was exceptionally cool or rainy, we might head for the nearest island, make a fire, and cook some of our sea food.

Ordinarily rain didn't stop us from spearfishing. The reef water was so clear that it took more than average rain clouds to make vision bad. The first time we started spearfishing in the rain, however, I thought it would prove a waste of time. When I got into the water and looked around it was full of wavy lines and everything was blurred as if I weren't wearing my face mask. But Siakong and Niraibui were diving without concern. Then I took a dive too and when my face reached about four feet below the surface, the water became its usual clear self. Then I realized that the blurring near the surface was the result of the fresh rain water mixing with salt water, something that always happens when two liquids of unequal densities are first put together. I've never come across an English word for it but German chemistry books refer to the phenomenon as *Schlieren*. So for spearfishing in the rain, one merely has to dive below the *Schlieren* layer and reach the homogeneous sea water to see clearly.

It was on such a day that we came across the largest giant clam I ever saw alive. Siakong and I were swimming across some open water toward the reef where the boat was anchored. Niraibui was sitting in it chewing betel nut and keeping his head dry under Siakong's straw hat. We swam along, diving now and then below the *Schlieren* layer for a look around.

Whenever I swim in deep open water, I keep glancing around through my face mask with a mingled feeling of fear and hope. I don't want to miss seeing it if a large shark should be cruising nearby. But on each of these dives I saw only empty water in all directions. Not the smallest fish was in sight. From above I could see Niraibui was still over one hundred yards away and I looked forward to reaching him and seeing the comforting walls of reef and the mass of familiar fish that would be swimming there. It is a strange feeling to swim underwater away from any signs of rock, coral, the bottom, or sea life. It's like swimming in the middle of the ocean. It was nice to be able to find Siakong in the water nearby.

I was getting a little ahead of Siakong, as he was stopping for deeper dives, when I heard him call me back.

"Nechan, come see here."

I swam over to him, dove under the *Schlieren*, and looked where he was pointing down below. I couldn't make out much until I was down a few more feet. Then I could see a sandy bottom and sitting in the sand was a clam. It looked like an average-size giant clam. However, there was nothing around to compare it with and I couldn't estimate the depth.

We swam to the surface and treaded water easily and forced a long series of deep breaths. We had been swimming for quite a while and I wasn't prepared for a deep dive. When I felt a little rested and saturated with fresh air, I nodded to Siakong. He started to dive toward the clam and I followed, swallowing to adjust my ears to the increasing pressure.

I've never measured how deep I can dive, but I know that at more than twenty-feet under, my face mask cuts into my head and my ears and nose feel uncomfortable. Usually I don't go much deeper for I have always found enough activity in the top twenty-five feet to keep me occupied and satisfied. But this time I followed Siakong until I felt I was well below my usual limit and I knew my breath wouldn't last descending any deeper. Perhaps if I had dived with a weight and not spent so much energy swimming downward, I might have been able to stand another ten feet—but I still wouldn't have been anywhere near bottom. From the depth I did manage to reach, I could see Siakong far below me getting smaller and smaller until he reached the clam.

Then I saw it was truly a giant.

Siakong looked like a midget beside the clam which seemed nearly four feet across. I saw him give it a kick to close the huge jaws which could have held all of Siakong with ease. And then I had to shoot for the surface. I was still panting heavily when Siakong finally came up with no sign of strain.

We got Niraibui to come over with the boat. The anchor wouldn't reach bottom. It hung loose, far above the clam. We couldn't improvise anything long enough to reach bottom and help us haul up the clam. Then the three of us dived toward the clam again but I stopped at a comfortable depth and clung to the dangling anchor while Niraibui continued on with Siakong. I doubted that even the two of them together could lift it an inch.

The clam's jaws were open again. Siakong reached it and kicked it shut. Niraibui hovered about Siakong's head for a second and then headed back for the surface, where we met, both well out of breath.

"*O kina ne!*" (It's a big one isn't it?) Niraibui exclaimed to me. His eyes were bloodshot and I figured he must have been drinking as well as chewing betel nut for his wind was usually much longer than mine.

Siakong still had not come up. Niraibui and I dived under again. As we descended I made out a sight that sickened me with horror. *Siakong was caught in the clam.*

The jaws of the gigantic mollusc were clamped tight and Siakong's arm was in it up to the elbow. Siakong wasn't moving. I expected Niraibui to dive all the way and at least attempt a rescue but the bleary-eyed fellow swam back to the surface. In the excitement my breath was shorter than ever. I came up gasping and started hollering at Niraibui in panic. My flimsy Japanese came out all mixed up and he looked at me surprised and then blankly. I felt helpless and desperate. Siakong was trapped and would be dead in a few seconds if we couldn't find some way to help him. How could Niraibui tread water there so calmly even if he was drunk!

Short of breath and good for nothing, I nevertheless adjusted my mask to dive again. But just then Siakong popped up beside us—panting but grinning! He lifted his arm out of the water, the one I had seen in the jaws of the clam, and held up the biggest adductor muscle I had ever laid eyes on.

I was doing a mixture of laughing and crying as the three of us climbed back into the boat. Niraibui of course had understood all along that the clam—which must have weighed at least a quarter of a ton—was impossible to lift off the bottom and that Siakong had broken the lip of the huge shell enough to reach into the clam and cut loose the adductor muscle with his knife. The two men got a big kick out of my fright.

"She was ready to kill me because I didn't try to save you!" Niraibui told Siakong, who howled with delight. I started to feel a little ridiculous, but when they went on to kid me unmercifully, I got angry. Finally they stopped and the rain which was still falling cooled me back to normal. Soon we all sat contentedly in the boat, munching on a delicious adductor muscle the size of a man's thigh. Niraibui and Siakong stuffed their mouths to keep from laughing any more.

I never saw Siakong spear a shark underwater, although several times he showed up with six- and seven-foot specimens neatly speared through the gills. He explained that the gills were the best place to spear a shark because the skin was too tough and if you missed getting the spear in, the shark might not give you the opportunity for a second try.

The same is true for moray eels. They stay mostly in their holes in the reefs, usually with only their ferocious-looking heads sticking out. You can get fairly close to one without endangering yourself if you don't wave an arm or leg carelessly in front of its lair. And it's safe to spear one through the head —if you're sure you won't miss.

The first time I saw a large moray I was full of confidence. Luckily I speared it neatly but then had to get Niraibui's help to get the four feet of writhing body off the spear. However, the more I continued to see of large morays, the less I toyed with them. I decided not to invite trouble without a good reason.

All of Siakong's spears were of the primitive hand type. He had none of the fancy arbaletes or CO_2 cartridged spearguns that shoot sixty feet through the water—the equipment of the hundreds of modern skin divers in Europe and the United States these days. When Siakong speared a fish his powerful arms were the only propelling force behind the spear. And the fish, though it be a shark, was then caught on one end of the spear while Siakong held on to the other.

I'm glad I first learned to use a hand spear. It made speargun fishing seem easy later on. And a simple hand spear needs no fancy repairs. It doesn't run out of "shells" and you don't lose twenty to one hundred dollars if you spear a big fish and lose your grip on the whole works. But of course a hand spear has its limitations—especially when you're not a diver like Siakong.

There was a time, however, when Siakong missed getting a rare specimen for me. The day started off wrong to begin with. It was a Sunday and we had invited Harry Uyehara to come along with us. We were to meet at Niraibui's boat at 7 A.M. but at 7:30 Siakong had not yet shown up. He was unreliable when it came to many things but not a spearfishing trip. He was always sober on such mornings no matter how wild had been his night before.

We finally went to his house.

"Siakong not here!" his wife said as she slammed the door in our faces. A little boy standing outside whispered to us, "He's in the calaboose."

"What's he in for?" we asked the jailkeeper when we reached Siakong's other quarters. We learned that the night before he had beaten up several men, including a policeman, and then had gone home and thrown his wife off the back porch into the taro patch. We also learned that this wasn't unusual for Siakong.

We were allowed to visit the jail. Through the bars we saw a big room with a number of drunks strewn about but Siakong was pacing the floor like a wild alert beast. When he saw us he came over and hung his head. *"Gomenasai, Nechan."* (Forgive me, big sister.)

Harry, one of the most diplomatic and well-liked persons in the Palaus, somehow talked the jailer into letting Siakong out in our custody and off we went to the reefs.

We went to a reef I hadn't seen before. The corals grew on a wide ledge about fifteen feet underwater. The ledge dropped off suddenly at its outer edge into what seemed to be deep ocean. Harry and Niraibui climbed back in the anchored boat when they had their fill of spearfishing while Siakong and I continued our favorite sport. There were a number of balloon fish and other easy-to-spear plectognaths around and we worked our way after them toward the edge of the reef.

I was struggling to get a triggerfish to fold up so I could pull him out of a crevice, when Siakong tapped me on the shoulder. He was pointing off the reef. As I watched I saw an incredible sight coming from the deep water.

At first I couldn't make out much except a light haze in the otherwise richly blue water. The haze was moving toward us. As it came closer it resolved into huge forms. It was like a flotilla of submarine dirigibles. There were so many I couldn't count them. Each was like a huge fat pig and had no color except a uniform gray-white.

They were fish undoubtedly, but a kind I had never seen before. They looked uncanny. Their heads were grotesque as if swollen and distorted. If I had seen only one I would have thought it was an anomaly. But here was a whole school of the weird beasts facing us. I had seen a head somewhat resembling theirs on only one other fish—the freakish-looking, artificially inbred lion-headed goldfish. But I knew these fish were not even distant monster relatives of any goldfish.

As they came closer we came up for air. "Are they dangerous? Can you spear one?" I asked Siakong and then quickly ducked under again to see how close they had gotten without waiting for his answer. Siakong gave me his usual reassuring look and then started swimming after them. In one movement the whole school made an about-face and headed back for deep water. They looked less formidable going in this direction and their tail ends were more fishlike than their monstrous heads. They had a fluffy look as they once again blended into just a light haze and disappeared—a herd of phantoms that Siakong could not catch up with.

Later Siakong told me he had seen these fish several times before and once they were fighting among themselves, butting with their heads. He had never succeeded in spearing one but he believed they were very powerful fish.

It was only recently that I decided these must have been a species of large wrasse, related to the group known as "sheepsheads," the adults of which grow fatty humps on their heads. While at the Red Sea, I saw a fisherman's photograph of a rare fish he had caught on a line. No one I consulted in Egypt could identify the fish but it resembled the school I had seen in the Palaus. From my notes and descriptions, Dr. L. P. Schultz of the Smithsonian Institute believes the species to be *Cheilinus undulatus*. He once saw a school of these in the Phoenix Islands.

Each appeared to be three to four feet long and the school reminded him of a flock of sheep. The ones I saw were easily this size. At the time, I estimated between four and five feet long, although I may have been overimpressionable then as many of us tend to be with "the fish that got away." Siakong didn't get close enough for me to compare and accurately estimate their size. However, I have since examined many pictures of sheepsheads and have never seen any with head swellings that approach those of the fish I saw with Siakong. I think they must have been exceptionally large adults to have developed such heads, if indeed they were any known species of sheepshead.

That same day when Siakong missed getting me a specimen of what was such a mystery fish for me, he and Niraibui put on an underwater turtle rodeo. They were in a clowning mood. Siakong caught hold of Niraibui's foot and tickled the bottom of it until Niraibui had to laugh out all his breath and almost drowned before Siakong let him go to the surface for air. They were having great fun. Then Niraibui spotted a large sea turtle resting quietly on the bottom and he sat on its back. Siakong latched onto Niraibui's back and they began taking turns knocking each other off the turtle and riding the bewildered animal around underwater. They could steer it any way they liked by holding the shell just behind the poor turtle's neck, pulling back to make it swim upward, pressing down to make it dive, and leaning sideways to make it bank and turn. All the while the turtle flapped its finlike legs desperately and strained its long

neck forward trying helplessly to get rid of the mischievous tor-
mentors.

Finally they brought the turtle on the boat. Niraibui was
pleased when I took his picture with it and I promised to give
him a print. I didn't know then, that that was our last trip with
him.

A few days later I asked Siakong if we could get together
with Niraibui for another fishing trip. "I don't think so," he
answered with a strange expression.

"What's the matter?"

"I think because he's dead," Siakong said sadly.

The whole story came out later. Niraibui had spied some
metal drums marked "alcohol" on a Navy truck. That was the
one word he could read in English. The fact that the complete
label read "methyl alcohol" didn't concern him. He punctured
a hole in one of the drums and drank to his heart's content and
end.

His widow sold his boat immediately. There was no other
motor boat available to me and thereafter Siakong and I had to
go to the reefs in outriggers. It took very long so we went only
on Sundays.

As my weeks in the Palaus came to an end, Siakong asked
when I would be back again. "Perhaps many years later," I said
because I hated to tell him, "Probably never." "That's O.K.,
Nechan, I'll still be a good spearfisherman when I'm eighty."
And he might have been, too. But a few years later I learned
that Siakong, after being released from a long stretch in jail,
went on a fishing trip, took a deep dive after a turtle, and never

came up again. The area was combed by other divers but they couldn't find a sign of him nor a clue to his disappearance. Perhaps with his great skill in the water, Siakong found a way to stay alive underwater indefinitely and just decided not to bother

GIANT CLAM

coming back to a world that was constantly throwing him in the calaboose. He may still be happily swimming around those reefs that he loved so much, playing with the turtles and fish. Who knows what the story of his mysterious disappearance will be when the Palauan children of today tell it to their grandchildren?

11

Fishes I Didn't Get

I went on two wild goose chases in the Palaus. One was to Geklau for a rabbit fish; the other was to Kayangel for a cowfish. That I was unable to obtain the fish I sought, didn't make these trips total failures. They were, in fact, among the most interesting of my fishing ventures.

"It is poisonous."
"It is not poisonous."
"It *is!*"
"It is *not!*"

Although I couldn't understand a word of Palauan, I'm sure that was the gist of what the two native fish authorities of Koror said when my interpreter asked about the rabbit fish of Geklau.

The answers to my first inquiries about poisonous-to-eat fishes in the Palaus had led me to believe that only blowfishes came in this category. But then I heard rumors and vague stories about the *meas* caught in a bay near Geklau that was dangerous to eat. *Meas* is the Palauan name for the common rabbit fish or *Siganus* as it is called by ichthyologists and laymen of Arabic-speaking countries—*Siganus* being one of the few scientific names derived from the Arabic (actually *Sigan*). Rabbit fish are common throughout the tropical Indo-Pacific waters and the many species known are considered good eating by natives all over the world. It is well known that their strong fin spines are mildly poisonous to touch and that fingers pricked by them give a painful, toxic, though brief reaction. But from all that I knew until then their flesh was considered excellent eating. The native resturant on Koror often served me delicious broiled *meas*. But then I was told by several persons, including Siakong, that this same species in Geklau was poisonous. However, even Siakong was not sure of the nature of the poison and he told me to consult fishermen who were more familiar with that area. These two I finally rounded up did not agree. After much discussion with them, the interpreter thought he understood and summed up the story. The *meas* is not *really* poisonous in Geklau; it only causes the eater to become intoxicated and the danger lies in eating this Geklau fish when one has work to do which requires sober concentration!

The *meas* story sounded so fantastic that I decided it was worth a trip to Geklau to find out for myself.

It was possible to make the trip in a weekend. I took Siakong along, knowing that if anyone could get the fish I wanted, he could. Harry, the obliging interpreter, and Dr. Robert Enders, a SIM mammologist in Koror at the time, were also interested in seeing the Geklau area and we organized a small group to make the trip. An old friend, Yoshi Kondo, a malacologist on the SIM program, was said to be in the region of Geklau and so we sent word ahead that we would try to meet him there.

Geklau is a small entirely native village located north of Koror on the eastern coast of Babelthuap, the largest of the Palau Islands. We were able to hire a motorboat that got us there in five hours. We couldn't start until late afternoon but Siakong assured me it made no difference because he planned to spear the *meas* for me at night! And indeed, by the time we reached the famous bay outside of Geklau, anchored our boat, and poled across the shallow water toward the village on bamboo rafts, it was a pitch-black night.

Our men called out in Palauan and some native voices answered from the shore, guiding us in. Then, as I started to make out a silhouette of coconut trees growing larger, a familiar voice shouted at us, "Welcome to Geklau!" It was Yoshi.

He held a small torch as we disembarked at our destination. Yoshi introduced us to the village chief, a tiny old man wearing only a drab-colored loincloth. The chief mumbled Palauan greetings in a high voice and shook hands with each of us. There were a number of natives out to meet us. "It's a big event for them to entertain visiting scientists from the States," Yoshi told me. "And when I informed them that a lady ichthyologist was coming, the chief had them build a special private *benjo*, just for you!" I assured Yoshi that I was greatly honored and, after the long boat trip especially, a room to "powder my nose" was just what I could use.

Siakong lost no time in making all the necessary arrangements for night fishing and soon we were poling back over the bay in long bamboo rafts again, in search of the *meas*.

It was easier than I expected. Siakong stood at the front of the raft with a long spear while another native and I took turns holding a bright torch. The fish were sleeping in the weeds and, in that second when the light awoke and blinded one in our path and before it recovered enough to shoot off into the weeds, it was safely on Siakong's spear and headed for his mouth where it received a bite on its head that stilled it forever.

In less than an hour we had ample specimens. There were two species, a spotted form and a less common form that had fine orange horizonal lines. The latter they called *klesbuul*, distinguishing it from the more common *meas* which was the species I ate at Koror.

When we returned to the village, our supper was being prepared and we were led to our quarters for the night, a large one-room *abai* or men's clubhouse. There is an *abai* in almost every native village. It is usually the largest and grandest structure, used only by the men of the village and distinguished visitors. My visitor rating evidently took priority over my sex, which surprised me, because I knew the *abai* was supposed to provide one place in the village where men could escape women—especially fishermen in the night before a fishing trip when it was considered bad luck if they slept under the same roof with a woman.

Before supper I had a chance to talk to the natives of Geklau and get some firsthand information about their *meas*. Yoshi went off to clean some snail shells but Harry stayed to act as interpreter. My first question brought a very disappointing answer. The *meas* and *klesbuul* were not poisonous. Anyone could eat them, raw or cooked. Every specimen we had caught that night was harmless!

What about all these stories which told that the Geklau *meas* was dangerous to eat? Oh, that was quite true, they added, but only during a certain time of year, October to January, when the wind blows steadily over the bay from the east and a special green seaweed grows in great abundance. *Then,* whoever eats *meas* or *klesbuul* will lose his head, laugh or get angry, act silly, or perhaps vomit and get sleepy—as if he had drunk too much of what I guess is the Palauan equivalent of "kickapoo joy juice."

We questioned several fishermen and they all agreed on the nature of the reaction. The seaweed factor made the story seem plausible as rabbit fish are herbivorous and, if the seaweed contained some mild irritant, the fish might well concentrate the irritant in its flesh at the time the seaweed grows in abundance. The natives added that during the month of December especially, the flesh of the *meas* felt like an astringent on mere contact with one's lips.

Unfortunately I had come to Geklau in August, the "off season," when not even a sample of the seaweed could be obtained. The chief invited me to come back when the seaweed was "in bloom." *Meas* wasn't deadly then, only intoxicating, and for the sake of science, his men would gladly give a demonstration of its effects. But there was little chance I could ever make a trip to Geklau again.

In exchange for the village's kind hospitality, we gave the

chief the American food provisions we had brought. A can of beans, even canned fish, was a great delicacy to these people. After our native supper, which we ate off coconut leaves spread on the floor of the *abai*, I decided to make a little test on the fish we'd caught, just in case there might be some slight reaction at this time of year which an outsider, not used to eating the local fish, might be able to detect. I ate a *klesbuul*, thinking that Yoshi, as my oldest friend there, would help me and act as second guinea pig by eating the other species. Dr. Enders and Harry would be the controls, having eaten everything else we did except rabbit fish.

"Have some *sashimi?*" I asked Yoshi holding out a raw *meas.* I had forgotten he wasn't around when we learned the details about these fish.

"Are you kidding?" he asked taken aback. "That's the poisonous fish, isn't it? Say, there's a limit to what you can ask of your friends."

After my explanations, Yoshi was still dubious but he finally ate the fish.

That night as we were preparing to go to sleep in the *abai*, which I was sharing with six men, I was informed that the old chief was sending a chaperone for me. The chief's special considerations were amusing and touching, I thought. I was rather surprised, though, when the "chaperone" showed up. It was another man!

Oh yes, Yoshi and I are still alive. We didn't even get indigestion. The next day after a short period of underwater fishing, our original boat party headed back to Koror and Yoshi went off into the jungles on Babelthuap after more snails.

In my search for the cowfish, I went to Kayangel alone. The cowfish is a plectognath with two "horns" on its head and belongs to the family of boxfishes. I had already collected many

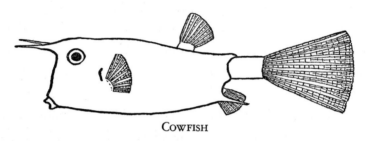

COWFISH

rare plectognaths, several of them new records for the Palaus, but I had yet to get a cowfish. A Japanese ichthyologist had reported finding one specimen in the Palaus—the only record in the scientific literature. But the Palauan fishermen all knew this fish well even though they admitted it was very rare. They called it the *karamasus*.

I asked all the fishermen on Koror to be on the lookout for a *karamasus* and made it known in the village that I would pay a reward for a specimen. Even little children tried to find the boxfish with two horns, but at the end of two months, none had been seen. The fishermen suggested I go to a big reef off the island of Kayangel; I would surely find a *karamasus* there. They told me what a wonderful reef it was, though few actually went there to fish as it was the most remote reef in the Palaus at the very northern tip of the island group. Cowfish are exceptionally good eating and seemed to be all fished out of the more popular reef fishing grounds in the Palaus. But the reef off Kayangel was seldom used except by two or three fishermen who lived in the tiny native village of Kayangel.

It was a full day's trip to Kayangel from Koror. I took a native boat that once a week made a series of stops along the west coast of Babelthuap. This time they would go still farther north, across a wide stretch of open ocean and drop me off at the crescent chain of four tiny islands known collectively as Kayangel. It would be at least a week before I could expect another boat to come and pick me up. It was not convenient for any of my native or SIM friends on Koror to accompany me for this length of time. But I was sure, from the stories about the big Kayangel reef, that I would have a great deal to occupy my time there for a week or two. And from past experiences with natives, I was sure I would have no trouble getting along with the villagers of Kayangel even though I knew none of them.

About twenty natives met our boat when our small crew, which had dwindled down to half a dozen, reached the dock at Kayangel. The reception was cooler than I expected. When I told them I had come to fish and asked if there was a fisherman who would help me, they all turned to one man. He had sharp cheekbones and wore the top of a stocking around his forehead holding in a mass of black curly hair. He answered me in Japanese: Everyone was busy and there were no fishermen at Kayangel!

Well, there was no need to force myself on these people the first day I arrived. I *did* come as an unannounced stranger—an odd one at that, for the women in these islands never go swimming, much less fishing.

But I soon found a friend. Siakong had told me that his sister lived in Kayangel. I saw a husky young woman whose features strongly reminded me of Siakong. When I told her I was Siakong's friend, she picked up all my belongings, loading a heavy box of equipment containing bottles of formalin, alcohol, rotenone, etc. on her head and without a word or motion toward me she walked into the woods. I followed her.

It was dark now. She led me to a large strongly built shack with a high pointed roof and a bamboo floor raised almost three feet off the ground. She made me climb in and then lit a kerosene lamp and placed it on the floor next to a sleeping mat. She still had no expression on her face and wouldn't even look into mine. I tried to talk to her but she left quickly and disappeared into the darkness outside.

She came back later and placed in the entrance of the shack a tin plate with bananas and tapioca and a large blue china bowl with hot fish soup. Then she was gone again. After waiting a while, I ate the food, then took a short walk. I heard voices off in the woods and saw some light shining through the entrance to another large shack. But I decided to return to the one allotted to me. I blew out the lamp and went to sleep on the mat.

During the night I was awakened a few times. In the moonlight I saw figures come into the shack but none came near me. In a far corner a child whined for a short time and then a female voice hushed it. Once I was awakened by heavy snoring. I felt very tired yet strangely excited. It is really true, Genie—you living with a group of natives on a South Sea island? How will it work out? I fell asleep again and dreamed of a reef with thousands of fish—and every one was a *karamasus*.

Much later I awoke again as three men were leaving the house. I crept over to the doorway and saw them walk through the woods to the dock and in the first gray light of morning I watched them through the trees as they took the boat I'd come on out to sea for her return trip to Koror.

That was my first night as guest in the home of Uredekl, the youngest sister of Siakong. I lived with her for the rest of my stay at Kayangel and we became great friends. Once she got over her shyness and started talking to me, I found she was quite a conversationalist. We stayed up every night till after midnight talking together and with her friends. Sometimes we visited other homes and they told me stories about the Palaus and Kayangel and their belief that the whole series of islands rose out of the sea in one night.

One evening Uredekl took me to see the ruler of Kayangel, a very old chieftainess with many bracelets on her wrinkled, thin arms and pendulous breasts which hung over her skirt as she sat on her bamboo floor and talked to us. She spoke only Palauan but Uredekl translated to me in Japanese. I had brought the chieftainess some soap and canned food and she ceremoniously brought out a warm bottle of Coke. Uredekl knocked off the rusted cap on the ladder we had climbed to reach the high floor of our hostess' grass shack. We passed the Coke among us and I felt as honored as if a hostess back in the States had opened her best bottle of brandy on the occasion of my visit.

The village had two *abais* and one night Uredekl took me into one, and with her kerosene lamp we went over the carvings in the wood on the walls. They told many stories; the two main themes were fishing and sex. There was no written language. The stories were told in a series of pictures and there seemed to be no censorship. The drawings on the whole were decorative in design and color although the lines were crude and simple and a bit shocking at first. The fish depicted were difficult to recognize as they bore few details. I made out the generalized forms of a shark, a ray, and a barracuda. I searched the other fish drawings for a possible *karamasus* but could find no fish with horns. The greatest details were in the pornographic series where the parts of the drawings that bore out the theme of the story were greatly exaggerated and further emphasized with a bright red dye.

A few evenings Uredekl and I stayed at home with her little son, Thomas. We entertained in the "kitchen," a separate tin shack where we cooked on an open stone hearth by burning coconut husks under a metal stand that held Uredekl's single large pot. We ate on the floor using our fingers and poor Thomas was always being scolded for "eating like a chicken." The food was put on large leaves except the hot dishes which could be served in two tin plates or the blue soup bowl. We often had fish soup which Uredekl flavored with the excellent lemons that were grown on Kayangel.

Cleaning up was no chore. The large pot was never washed— it just accumulated flavors. Thomas was the automatic dishwasher, a job he didn't mind. He'd quickly gather up the leaves and garbage and throw them in the rubbish pile to be burned later. Then he'd run down to the beach with the dishes, rinse them in the sea (sometimes by taking them for a swim—he seldom wore clothes and hence was always attired for a splash in the ocean), scrubbing out the grease with sand. After supper Uredekl liked to stretch out on the kitchen floor and relax. I would join her and later other women would drop in and sit beside us and start chewing betel nut.

All the women chewed betel nut which grew on high trees around the grounds. I had a try at it too. It was the evening when a group of native women came to visit us and Uredekl introduced me to them for the first time. We sat around the kitchen rather stiffly. Then during an awkward silence (my Japanese was going over poorly anyhow), one of the women took out her bag of betel chewing accessories and offered me a nut. It was one of those hospitable, friendly gestures I couldn't turn down. So I took the nut. She hastened to give me the green leaf that went with it, sprinkling a little white powder on the leaf. When she tried to add a half a cigarette to this I managed a polite refusal by quickly rolling the nut in the powdered leaf and shoving it all in my mouth as I'd seen it done. I forced a smile. The ladies seemed pleased and all began fixing their own concoctions.

After a few chews my mouth was full of saliva, which works up quickly and turns blood red when it reacts to the betel nut. The ladies were spitting expertly through narrow cracks in the floor that I knew I couldn't make.

Uredekl caught me on my first swallow. "Don't do that, it

will make you very sick." The others agreed and warned me too. One shot a red stream out the doorway. I was closer to it than she was so I tried the same. I didn't make it and my mouth had been so full that it looked as if someone had spilled a cup of beet juice on Uredekl's kitchen floor.

The women laughed good-naturedly. "Not like that, like this!" each seemed to tell me as she followed with a demonstration of her skill. Unfortunately I had reached the stage where I was not in the mood for a spitting lesson. My stomach felt awful. I got up and tried to walk the few steps to the door but my head was dizzy and I staggered my way. I sank to the floor at the doorway where I stuck my head out and got rid of the juicy red mass from my mouth. Uredekl propped me against the wall and rubbed my head and the others acted very sympathetic too, repeating what seemed to be, "She shouldn't have swallowed."

After this episode I was at least accepted into their informal social circle and we all felt at ease with each other. They didn't offer me betel nut again, except jokingly, but were anxious to show me everything of interest on their island. They invited me to go to the woods with them the next day.

The women of Kayangel are hard workers. In addition to their domestic chores, they work long hours in the woods preparing copra. It takes strength and skill to open and husk coconuts at the rate they work. One blow of an ax would split a coconut in half. Three or four knife strokes would separate the white "meat" from each half shell. I offered to "help," but I won't tell you how many ax and knife strokes I had to use per coconut nor after how many coconuts my blistered hands had to give up. I didn't even offer to carry the coconut meat to the stands where it was spread and dried in the sun. Those women must have steel necks. It took all my strength to help one woman lift a coconut-laden basket onto the head of another woman, who then walked over a mile through the rough woods balancing the enormous weight while my head felt as if it were sinking into my shoulders just from watching her.

I spent only this one day in the woods with them. Early the next morning, the man with the stocking holding in his black hair came to take me fishing. I learned his name was Eminio and that he was the "number one" fisherman in Kayangel. During the rest of my days in Kayangel I went to the big reef with Eminio. His two young sons usually came along and paddled the canoe we took to reach the reef. Sometimes an old fisherman also accompanied us. He advised us about many things but was too old to do much active fishing himself except when we caught octopi from holes in a shallow part of the reef.

Spearfishing around the big reef was a wonderful experience. I learned many new things including the unusual behavior of a rare plectognath. I was chasing a group of small pufferfish that I'd never seen before—a species with unusual brown saddle marks across its back. I speared one, then followed the group to get another. As I swam after them, I noticed that one looked slightly different at certain times. When it stopped swimming, it lifted an appendage on its head where puffers have no appendage. I had to get that particular fish. I chased it until I was almost exhausted but when I finally speared it, I was well rewarded. It was not a pufferfish at all! It was a filefish that so perfectly mimicked, in size, shape, coloring, and swimming movements, the poisonous puffers it swam with, that only on the rare moments when it lifted the "file" on its head did it give itself away.

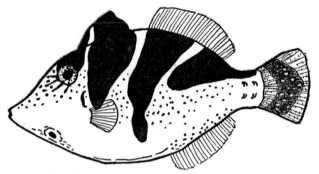

A FILEFISH THAT MIMICS A POISONOUS PUFFER

One time, paddling back from the reef, Eminio suddenly spotted something below us and called my attention to it. On the white sandy bottom there was a large black patch perhaps twenty or more feet across. As the shadow of our canoe passed over it, it came to life. It was a giant manta ray. A smaller black patch behind it came to life too and in a moment the pair of rays seemed to fly away in the water below, their great "wings" flapping slowly but propelling them with speed.

A week in Kayangel went by too fast. Days on the reef with Eminio and evenings with Uredekl and her friends was a period of time that I hated to see end. It was a sad sight for me when the boat from Koror was spotted on the horizon.

I've never minded that Eminio and I didn't even see a cowfish. Oddly enough, months later, when I was back working in the Department of Animal Behavior of the American Museum of Natural History, the Department of Amphibians and Reptiles sent me word that they had received a collection of reptiles from Peter Hill on Koror. There happened to be one fish in among the specimens. Did I want it?

I went to the reptile department and looked at the fish. It was a beautiful specimen of a full-grown *karamasus*. Mr. Hill had caught it himself in a shallow lagoon near the Memorial Station.

12

South of the Palaus

To the southeast of the Palaus is a group of five tiny islands. Geographically they seem to be part of the East Indies, but actually they are the most remote of the Caroline group and hence come under the jurisdiction of the U.S. Trust Territory. Little is known about these islands. The total population is less than three hundred and the natives speak a language, all their own, that the finest libraries on linguistics cannot help you with.

Three or four times a year, from the base at Koror, the Navy sends out a ship on a "field trip" to visit these islands and check conditions there. At such times the Island Trading Company buys copra and handicraft from the natives, who in turn buy cigarettes, cloth, canned goods, etc. from the Island Trading Company. This is the only contact the natives have with the outside world.

I felt very lucky to be permitted along on a Navy field trip to these islands. Lt. Stille was in charge of native affairs during this trip. In addition to the regular crew and native travelers, there were two Jesuit priests and myself. The kind skipper of the ship, Lt. Shannon, insisted on turning over his own cabin to me because, he said, it had the most privacy and a large desk where I could write up my notes undisturbed.

Our first stop was Sonsorol—small twin islands, together less than a square mile in area. A wide skirt of shallow, jagged reef, which dropped suddenly two hundred fathoms into very deep ocean, surrounded each island. The ship had to keep circling the whole day as there was no spot where it could safely anchor.

Little brown native men wearing loincloths came to meet us in outrigger canoes and we went ashore with them to the village on the southern island where some 120 natives were living.

We were greeted enthusiastically. The men and women rushed to Father Lewis who was known to them from previous trips. Each in turn grabbed Father Lewis' hand, bent over and sniffed it, then backed away making the sign of the cross. It was Father Walter's first trip to these islands but he explained to me, "That must have originated from the habits of the early Spanish missionaries. Their sentiment is what counts. Whether they sniff or kiss the hand makes little difference and it might even be offending to try to correct them."

When Father Lewis introduced Father Walter to the natives, mainly by gestures and the word "Padre," they did the same to Father Walter.

Most of the natives came over and shook hands with the rest of us. The men wore loincloths or shorts and a few had trousers and shirts which looked like parts of old uniforms. The women, although barefooted like the men, were obviously dressed up for us. They wore cotton dresses, pieces of cheesecloth pinned on their heads mantilla style, and fresh flowers through the large holes in their ears. They regarded me with much interest and curiosity, and with friendly expressions and gestures they talked to me with words I couldn't understand. My simple greetings to them which I tried in English, Spanish, and Japanese brought no recognition from them. But it didn't seem to matter. They put a wreath of large lilylike flowers around my head, took me by the hands and pulled me around visiting their houses. These were made of grass tops with sides of neatly woven coconut fronds. They offered me endless quantities of fresh coconut milk, one of the few really refreshing drinks that can be enjoyed tepid in hot weather.

I wanted to learn the names of some of the women so I pointed to myself and said, "Genie," and then pointed inquiringly to each of them. Their eyes lit up with understanding and then each pointed to herself with a big smile and said, "Obis." They made me say the word too, several times, until I had the intonation just right. Everyone was "Obis," including me, and we used this term often. It is the only word of their language that I learned. But I think it is also the nicest one because later Father Lewis told me it means "friend."

When I returned from visiting, Father Lewis was just starting Confession. The natives were queued up waiting to kneel before the priest in the shade of a large grass hut.

"Father Lewis must be able to understand their language,"

I remarked to Stille. "He certainly looks as if he knows what they're telling him."

"Go a little closer and see how he does it," Stille suggested. I did and saw that Father Lewis was nodding comprehendingly while the confessor was merely holding out fingers. Father Walter then told me, "The old Spanish missionaries, who must have lived years among them, taught these natives about Confession and the Ten Commandments. Now, even with the language barrier, a native can still tell the Father which commandments he broke and how many times he broke them, by the number of fingers he holds out."

Fortunately for me, the top spearfisherman on the island was not a Christian, so when Father Lewis started Mass for the Christian natives I went out hunting for plectognaths.

Our first specimen was a spectacular, Halloween-decorated triggerfish. It had bright orange lips and a black body with large white spots on the lower sides. It was the first of its kind I had seen but I recognized it from illustrations in Japanese books about poisonous fishes. Limited to gestures only, I asked the fisherman if this species could be eaten. I gathered one could eat it, at least in Tobe. Before we went into the water, I had drawn pictures in the sand of the various plectognaths I wanted, not sure however if the fisherman understood. But he speared this rare triggerfish before I even saw it and I found that I didn't have to point out the plectognaths to him.

On an island more primitive than the Palaus, I was surprised to find that this native diver was using a more advanced type of spear than any I'd seen used by Palauans. The shaft and spear were of separate pieces and the latter was shot from a rubber sling tied on the shaft. It worked very well for the native but my few attempts with it were unsuccessful. Time was too short for practicing so I used the simple spear I had with me.

After an hour of spearfishing we returned to the village for lunch. Low tide had exposed a few small pools in the reef which I poisoned. The fishes were much the same as those I'd got from the Palaus but it was still of value to have a sample from an island where ichthyologists had not collected before.

Most of the afternoon the natives were occupied loading copra on the ship's whaleboats. Hundreds of bags had been stored in a canoehouse on the beach, ready for the ship's arrival. The long process of loading all the bags gave me a chance for some more late-afternoon spearfishing.

Unfortunately the tide was coming in fast and the water was rough. The best place to spearfish is where a fringing reef starts to drop. But this point was so abrupt around Sonsorol that I had an uncomfortable feeling when the native diver got out of sight and I had to swim along, well away from the edge of the jagged reef to keep from being bounced on it by the roughening sea. The wall of coral was a beautiful sight but when I peered down through the clear water at the sheer drop it took, it gave me the feeling of looking down the side of a skyscraper. And the realization that gigantic sharks must come in very close to such reefs made me keep glancing over my shoulder.

I chased a tiny pufferfish that I had never seen before, into a sandy alcove in the reef. But I lost track of him when I looked down and saw a monster grouper of at least eight hundred pounds. It was just lying in the sand looking up at me with that lazy gentle expression of large groupers, which are members of the sea bass family of harmless fishes. It would have been a cinch to spear, like hitting the side of a barn, but what would I have done with the monster when it started kicking on the end of my comparatively flimsy spear?

We continued to watch each other, the fish regarding me with a careless nonchalance while I looked over his great form with awe. A sure shot through his spinal cord would probably do the trick, I thought. As I searched around for my diver I saw *Schlieren* forming in the water. I stuck my head up into pouring rain and heard someone calling.

Father Walter was wading out on the reef toward me. "Stille wants us all to go back to the ship immediately. Bad storm coming up."

I cut my legs climbing back on the reef as the breakers dashed me quickly toward shore. We ran for the last whaleboat. Another, loaded with copra, capsized in front of us and the rich dried meat of thousands of coconuts plunged to the sea bottom far below. We left this island unceremoniously with only the most hurried thanks and farewell to its kindly inhabitants.

Our next stop was Tobe, an island that sits three degrees above the equator, where "monkey-men" are made. The Island Trading Company sells more of these strange, squatting statuettes than any other piece of native handicraft from the Caroline

Islands. Hundreds are turned out by a handful of native sculp-
tors in the few months' interval between Navy field trips to
this island. The figures are carved from driftwood and almond-
shaped bits of pearly white shell with round centers of black
tar are inserted into the head of the figure to serve as eyes.
These eyes have a penetrating stare which is almost hypnotic if
you keep looking into them. (The members of my family were
later delighted with these souvenirs—all except grandma who
finally returned hers because "I don't like his eyes watching
me all the time.")

We had excellent weather at Tobe. I spearfished with a
native diver and his little boy for four hours, reaping a large
collection of plectognaths from the fish-packed fringing reef.
But I remember Tobe most for its black-tipped sharks.

I was swimming with a string load of fish tied around my
waist, some of them still oozing a little blood from the spear
wounds. And then I discovered a small shark following just a
few feet behind me. I started untying the string from my waist
and called out to the native diver. He wasn't the least perturbed
but rather more annoyed that I had stopped him from spearing a
large chocolate filefish. He merely took the string of fish from
me, tied it to his own string, and went back to where he had
been while the shark nosed along after him. I knew then that
the shark couldn't have been dangerous for these native divers
are the first to warn you when you are near a venomous scorpion
fish or a stinging coral. But still I was startled when I started
for shore and found my path blocked by a larger member of
the same species—easily recognized by black tips on its fins.

I decided to make a round-about detour but still another black-tipped shark came along. The water was barely four feet deep so I stood up, keeping my head and one hand holding a dead fish out of the water and tiptoed toward the shore while the large forms swimming around seemed to take little notice of me.

Merir was undoubtedly the most unusual island we visited during this field trip. It was the island of the outcast aged.

"Do they really abandon old people on Merir?" I asked Stille unbelievingly. I had heard that the people on the surrounding islands brought their aged relatives here—and left them.

"It's not as bad as it sounds; wait and see. The only bad part about Merir is the large pond in the middle of the island. It breeds mosquitoes. The last time we were here four months ago they were getting pretty bad."

As with the other islands the ship had to stay away from the shore. When we came as close to it as the skipper thought safe, a boat was lowered to take us in. No native canoes came out to meet the ship this time.

"Better wear more than that—a long-sleeved shirt, if you got one," one of the sailors warned me as he adjusted a contraption over his head made of thick netting. I noticed Stille had put on long pants for this island. I went back to my room for a jacket and slacks.

As we approached the shore we saw a light smoke rising from the beach and three old men were standing there to welcome us. We rowed our boat toward the remains of an old stone dock and anchored it beside a fish trap made of coral rocks in the form of a large arrow pointing out to sea. Mosquitoes were already buzzing around us. The old men helped us ashore and gave each of us a smoking coconut husk and a fan made of woven coconut leaves. The smoke was supposed to help keep away the mosquitoes but we practically danced our way to the tiny village, swatting our faces and bodies with the handy fans.

"This is really awful, worse than ever," Stille said. "We'll have to bring barrels of oil to pour over that pond next trip." But the three old men walked along with us as if immune to the hungry insects.

The village consisted of a half dozen small shacks, one of which was the chapel. The census of Merir was eleven, and ten showed up for Mass. Father Lewis delivered the Mass as fast as he could but the smoke from all the burning coconut husks that the natives had put around the altar to make him more "comfortable" had him coughing and gagging on his words while tears ran out of his eyes.

After Mass we led a blind man back to his shack and there saw the eleventh inhabitant of Merir. She was his wife, a woman well over eighty. She was lying on the floor on a mat as these natives do when they sleep. Her eyes were closed and she didn't move. A lizard ran down from her shoulder as we approached her.

"Is she alive?" I asked, swallowing a few times.

"Those mosquitoes are feeding on something," Stille said, with a slight shudder, as he looked at the exposed parts of her body which were covered with a network of the living insects.

There was no point to brushing them off as hungrier ones would only replace them.

"She hasn't long to live, I'm glad we reached here today," said Father Lewis as he bent over her. He started praying. The old woman weakly tried to lift one hand though her eyes remained closed and no other part of her moved. Father Lewis took her hand and helped her make the sign of the cross. Her blind husband groped along the floor until he reached her head. He patted her hair slowly and gently while the prayer was continued.

I walked outside the shack for I could hardly control myself any longer. "Oh Stille, I thought you said it wasn't so bad here."

"Death is seldom a nice sight anywhere. You happened to come at an exceptionally unpleasant time. Come on, let's go have a chat with the chief. He'll cheer you up some."

The chief was a funny old fellow. He spoke a few words of English, very exactly and very proudly. He seemed quite content to face his remaining days on this island. He took us around and showed us the various traps they used to catch fish, and the small field where they grew taro and tapioca. And they had fresh fruit handy—mangoes, bananas, and the all purposeful coconut tree.

Three old women were sitting around in a congenial group. Two were weaving baskets and mats and the third was shredding a coconut. They looked up and smiled at us, their faces a mass of wrinkles, yet not as pathetic as the faces of old people I'd seen before. Each of them in this small community of Merir had some essential job to do. Each was needed and they all depended on each other.

"The boys want to go back to the ship as soon as possible. I don't think you'll find a guide to take you spearfishing here," Stille said, urging me to leave. And so, still swatting at our now swollen and itching skin, we left Merir while wrinkled, thin, but still strong arms waved us off.

13

Field Trip to Ulithi

I was permitted to go on one other Navy field trip just before I left the Palaus. This was to the northernmost group of islands in the Carolines: Ngulu, Fais, and the Ulithi Atoll. They were truly romantic islands. We left Koror at high tide on September 20. I knew two of the other passengers from the previous field trip—Lt. Stille, who was in charge of native affairs again, and Father Walter who came along to give spiritual guidance to the natives of these islands. We took a Navy transport headed by Lt. Parnell.

The first night at sea most of us gathered aft for the ship's popular evening diversion—an outdated, second-grade, black-and-white movie. This was shown on a canvas screen behind which the tropic sun had set in lavish color just a short time before—practically unnoticed. Brilliant sunsets at sea apparently get to be monotonous for sailors, who never tire of seeing movies. In addition to the main feature, there was a "sing" short during which the bouncing white ball was followed by the lusty voices of the Navy men, Father Walter, and even a few of the native passengers. During the "girls only" section, my first yell subsided to a weak solo as I felt the rest of the audience turn to watch with amusement the lone female in their midst.

After the movie, Father Walter invited Lt. Stille and me to share some of his bouillon-cube soup. This gave me the opportunity to ask about the islands we were going to visit. Lt. Stille had made this trip several times and knew the chiefs of all the islands. To Father Walter, these were "his islands," where he had already befriended the natives and was fast learning their language, and where he hoped to preach the gospel for the rest of his life. We talked about natives, God, and fishes for over an hour before turning in.

At 6:30 the next morning a knock at the door announced breakfast. We weren't due at Ngulu for a few hours, and so after breakfast I sat at the bow and watched the flying fishes shoot out from under the ship.

We sighted the little island on the southern tip of the large Ngulu Atoll about 10 A. M. The last census, taken three months before, reported fifty-two natives here. Ngulu was similar to the other islands I'd seen on the southern field trip—at first just a clump of coconut trees on the horizon seven miles away, and twenty minutes later a village of grass huts peeking out at one point. Coffee-skinned natives were slipping their little outriggers off the white coral beach into the shallow, pale green water over the wide fringing reef. Out past the reef they paddled into the sudden deep blue waters to meet our ship and welcome us. I could hardly wait to get ashore and joined the first returning outrigger.

FROGMAN OF NGULU

Unlike most of the other islands, Ngulu did not sell copra. Its major products were sculptured wooden figures which the Island Trading Company called "frogmen." Actually they were heavy-browed, triangular-faced pregnant women symbolizing fertility. Several hundred figures ranging from a few inches to nearly two feet were lined up on the beach. Some were carefully carved in bold and interesting lines, whereas others were obviously chipped out hastily to meet the new large demand of the I.T.C. which was selling them back at Koror like hot cakes. Lt. Stille wisely bought only the well-carved figures and in his unoffending yet critical manner and gesticulating pidgin English let the natives know he was after quality as well as quantity.

The natives were exceedingly friendly. The women and children came up and patted my arms and held my hands. "You're probably the first white woman they've seen," Stille chuckled. The native women were highly interested in my bathing suit and fingered the gaily colored material with curiosity and amusement. Stille consulted an interpreter and then reported, "They think your shorts are immodest and your bra superfluous." I couldn't be sure if he was kidding or not. My outfit was a contrast to theirs. The women and girls wore heavy, bulky grass skirts almost to their ankles, and some had leaves and flowers around their heads or stuck through large holes in the lobes of their pierced ears. Their skirts had the pleasant smell of dried grass—a practical garb for these people, for soap and cloth are rare items. Instead of wearing ragged, patched clothes that accumulate odors with soapless washings, they merely toss away soiled clothes and string together a new skirt.

One young girl had reddish-orange paint on her forehead and cheeks, but her hair was cut short like a boy's. "It helps to keep the bugs out," I was told. This little girl, whom I nicknamed "Red," put her hand in mine and did not let go until I went fishing. She took me for a walk through the village, which was beautifully clean and ready for Stille's sanitary inspection. Some of the grass huts had stone or wooden foundations, and almost all the pathways and ground surrounding the huts had been covered with white coral pebbles. Garbage was carefully thrown into holes, where it was burned from time to time and finally covered over. These were teachings that the natives obediently accepted from the Navy, and they understood that the rules were for their own benefit.

At high tide Stille rounded up two Ngulu spearfishermen who spoke Japanese, and so I detached myself from Red and went out on the reef with them.

The tide began going out slowly, but it was still fine for spearfishing. We started from the north side of the island and worked toward the west. The fringing reef around this island was the most beautiful I had ever seen. Colored corals grew abundantly close to the shore, and with them were the rich fauna and flora that are usually found only toward the outer edge of fringing reefs. This was probably because the reef around this island slopes less abruptly into the deep water outside and ravines cut into the reef at frequent intervals. Just a few yards from shore we dropped into one of these ravines. It went down suddenly about five feet, and then we followed the ravine as it deepened to about thirty feet just at the edge of the fringing reef. Here it widened into a spacious submarine coral garden.

The younger of my spearfishermen scraped his arm on some coral while chasing a tiny poisonous puffer. He didn't seem to think the fish I was after were worth it and he left, saying that he was too tired to continue. The older man, who was more skilled and interested in the odd assortment of fish I desired, stuck it out for several hours, laughing heartily when I grew enthusiastic over a little fish that was a rare specimen for my collection but seemed completely worthless to him. At one point we saw a beautiful big orange triggerfish—the largest triggerfish I'd seen and a species I hadn't yet caught. I pointed to it excitedly, and through my face mask I saw my spearfisherman start after this fish that presented more of a challenge to him. The fish swam downward, out of our alcove to where the reef took a deep drop. The fisherman dived after it with his spear poised for a lunge. He was down about twenty feet when a large shark swam slowly past above him. He saw the shark but with no alarm came to the surface, took a breath, and made a deeper dive in the same place to recover his spear, which had missed its target. The shark seemed about eight feet long, and I was growing uneasy about its return when I suddenly spotted a pair of barracuda, each about four feet long, approaching from my right.

It was the first time I'd seen barracuda in the Pacific reefs and the first time I'd seen any of that size so close to me in the water. My spearfisherman had followed the orange triggerfish around a wall of coral and was out of sight. I remembered an armchair discussion in which I had expressed my belief that barracuda do not normally attack forms as large as man and that when they do, it is because they do not see the form as a whole but are attracted to some small light areas such as the palms of hands or soles of kicking feet, which stand out as ruptive patterns on an otherwise dark body. Shiny rings and bracelets are thought to be especially attractive. And aren't barracuda caught by fast-trolling, small, bright lures? As I treaded water, watching the two menacing forms, I reminded myself that I was deeply tanned, wearing a dark bathing suit, black *tabi* shoes, and no jewelry, and I was barely moving— but none of these thoughts comforted me.

The barracuda had stopped about six yards away and were resting almost motionless near the surface. I backed away easily from the center of the alcove to the rim of a wall of coral that reached within a few feet of the surface. I stood on this, watched the razor-toothed pair of fish through my face mask, and longed to see my spearfisherman. There was a loud splash in the water behind me. Startled and quite terrified, I turned, only to see among the bubbles in the disturbed water the nude lower half of a young girl who had just dropped in next to the hull of an outrigger. I put my face mask above the water and saw Red's painted face laughing at me. What a welcome sight! She was hanging to the side of an outrigger in which she had left her bulky grass skirt. I was overjoyed to see her, and she felt it and swam happily toward me. I pointed to the barracuda before it occurred to me that she couldn't see them very well without a face mask or goggles. I motioned to her to climb into the boat, and after a last look at the large silver forms still in the alcove, I quickly followed. Some distance away I saw my spearfisherman come up for a breath. We called him over, but when I looked again the barracuda were gone, and his only reaction to my serious description of them was a giggle and the supposed-to-be comforting Japanese phrase, "*Abunakunai* (not dangerous)."

We paddled the outrigger a good distance from the alcove to continue our fishing. When we returned to the village, we found Stille was anxious to return to the ship, and we left hurriedly. I gave the usual salary to my spearfisherman plus a gift of cigarettes, and for Red I left some candy and chewing gum. Back on the ship and ready to pull away from Ngulu, I spied Red and my spearfisherman among the group of outriggers bobbing about the stern of the ship, waving a last good-by to me. It didn't seem that our acquaintance had been for less than a day and that we'd exchanged but a few words of broken Japanese.

We arrived at Fais near noon of the following day. The native men came out to meet us in large outriggers of bright orange and black. When we reached shore, all the high chiefs of the island were sitting cross-legged in front of a large grass-covered *abai*. Stille presented me to them, and I shook hands with each of them during an exchange of curious glances. Their faces were serious and dignified, and they presented a weirdly beautiful picture. Their bodies were heavily tattooed from the neck down with vertical stripes and designs of various types, some of which I made out to be fish. One old chief had apparently tinted his gray hair and beard with the same shade of dye that "Red" on Ngulu had used on her face.

During most of the day the chiefs hardly budged from their original position. They chatted with us (two could speak some

English), smoked the cigars Stille brought them, and acted as
overseers while the other men rushed about loading copra,
bringing us coconuts to drink, and waiting on the chiefs. Aside
from the more elaborate tattooing and headdress, most of the
chiefs could be readily distinguished from the common natives
by their bulging bellies, fat bodies, and smoothly rounded and
relaxed limbs, as compared to the slim, taut, muscular bodies
of the "workers."

I became curious to see the women of this island. Stille
and Father Walter had told me that instead of grass skirts, the
grown women here wore laboriously hand-woven cloth skirts
called lava-laps. But there were no women around, and we had
been on the island for over an hour. Some time later I noticed
that one by one they were slipping out from behind coconut
trees, walking in a peculiar, crouched-over position with their
backs almost parallel to the ground. Stille then told me they had
to walk like that in the presence of men—a law of feminine
obsequiousness on that island that I was brazenly breaking!
Ignorance of the law is no excuse, but the chiefs were lenient
with me and never said a word.

I joined a few of the women sitting under some trees, and
soon a large crowd of them gathered around. None of them
spoke Japanese. I started a sign-language conversation that
was accompanied by sympathetic giggles and laughter, and the
women reciprocated until we must have looked as though we
were playing a game of charades.

Most of the older women's forearms and legs were tattooed,
and they wore bracelets, beaded necklaces, and belts. The belts

held up their colorful lava-lap skirts, which were folded in such a manner that the loose edges met in front, forming an attractive hanging fringe. Each woman carried a good-sized "pocketbook" made of a woven coconut frond and containing paraphernalia similar, I guess, to what most of us are prone to tag about with us (paint for the face, cigarettes, etc.).

During a tour of the island, we came near a large grass hut with high fences on either side that led down the beach and part way into the water.

"You can go inside if you like but the rest of us have to wait here. No men allowed in there," Stille said mysteriously. But Father Walter added casually, "It's the women's menstrual house." I learned that at this time of the month the women are separated from the men and must live among themselves in these special quarters. Here they have no work to do; the other women even bring them prepared food. The women look forward to this time when they can relax and chat among themselves while escaping their usual chores. They often "fake" a few extra days. This house of segregation is part of an old custom that some say led jealous husbands to build the first *abai* where men only could get together and enjoy themselves.

Inside it was indeed a comfortable-looking place. Many thick mats lined the floor. One woman sat on an opened coconut husk which probably was the most absorbent material they had. Some women were weaving lava-laps with straw dyed a bright purple. They gave me instructions on weaving and offered me a snack of smoked fish that they were eating.

The "number one" chief offered his two finest fishermen to

help me with my collecting. We spent a profitable and enjoyable time spearfishing at the end of the fringing reef. When we returned, all the copra had been brought to the ship. Mass and Confession were over, and native affairs settled. The chiefs promised to stage a dance for us in the evening. We stayed for a supper of breadfruit, fish, and bananas with the natives, and then came the floor show. It was pitch dark by then, and a large bonfire was built on the beach in front of the *abai*. The evening was cool and damp. I'd given my dress to a chief's wife, who with the other women had greatly admired the bright-colored cotton print, and I was left wearing only my damp bathing suit. I welcomed the opportunity to push my mat into a warm, dry spot near the fire.

The men, I was told, would not dance because they were worn out from carrying the large sacks of copra, but the women were ready and willing to perform. They lined up in a row of fifteen. The center women were the oldest and obviously the leaders who knew the dances best. The breasts became higher and firmer toward the ends of the line, where the young girls made up in attractiveness what they lacked in dance training.

The dance started with the women stamping their feet in rhythm to a low chant. As the dance progressed, they hardly moved from their spot but turned in place, first to one side then the other and sometimes completely around—the sinuous movements of their bodies becoming increasingly emphasized. Their arms hung loosely much of the time, but sometimes they swayed in movements complementary to those of the body or they waved about in rag-doll fashion slapping the thighs and buttocks from time to time. The girls at the ends of the line frequently missed their cues to turn at the right time and obviously bluffed through the words to parts of the chant. But their improvisations were of ceaseless charm to Stille. Father Walter, however, accustomed to these dances on his home island of Yap, played with the children and was the most casual spectator at the weird dance held in the light of a bonfire. The excitement mounted as the chanting grew louder and higher in pitch, ending finally in a sudden and abrupt mass yell.

We applauded enthusiastically. Some of the entertainers acted as if we weren't there; a few glanced our way and then giggled self-consciously. Then all eyes went to the center woman, who cued off, and a second dance began. The women had prepared a limited number of encores, at the end of which they all walked away, and the bonfires, perfectly timed, petered out to just a warm glow.

In the darkness we bade farewell to the people, thanked the chiefs, and returned to our ship. We didn't attend the "Western" that was being shown aft but turned in early after some of Father Walter's bouillon.

The following day we arrived at the sausage-shaped atoll called Ulithi. Ulithi is composed of some forty-nine islands, but only seven are inhabited. The villages on each of these are headed by one or more chiefs, but the supreme ruler of the Ulithians—the chief of chiefs—was King Ueg.

Our first stop was on the island of Mog Mog, where the king lived. I had never dreamed that at my first meeting with a king I would be in bare feet, bathing suit, and pigtails, and the king in a G-string!

Word of his coming reached us shortly after our arrival on the island. I had heard that King Ueg had been a polio victim some years back and was now unable to walk. I expected him to be brought out on a royal platform carried on the shoulders of his subjects. Instead, a lone native approached us pulling a little rubber-tired wagon in which sat the King of Ulithi. The royal wagon was a rather funny sight, and the withered lower limbs of its occupant were pathetic: but Ueg's face itself was truly majestic. He had a fine straight nose with firm nostrils, sharp blue eyes, highly arched eyebrows, and thick, black, curly hair. The contours of his face were handsome. He looked dignified, wise, and kind, and although most of the time his expression was solemn, when he smiled it was with sincerity and warmth. Like the chiefs on Fais, he was heavily tattooed and wore a simple comb in his hair but no other decorations.

We stayed at Ulithi four more days, and in addition to Mog Mog we visited the islands of Asor and Fassari. King Ueg came along with us, and on each island he commanded the best spearfisherman to give me all the help I needed. Rows of rusted quonset huts—a leftover from the days of World War II when the Navy maintained a large base at this atoll—lay rotting among the coconut trees. Asor particularly had many of these eyesores unsuitable to a tropical island.

Fortunately, the important parts of my days were spent as usual in the least battle-scarred and most beautiful part of the South Seas—in the forests of corals and algae, where the graceful plumed heads of annelids and sea anemones three feet in diameter are the flowers, and fish and fishermen are the birds of the aquatic air.

Ulithi was the last place for my underwater explorations of the Pacific. From there it was straight back to Koror where, after a few days of packing all my specimens, I started the long plane ride back to New York.

Back in my laboratory at the American Museum of Natural History there is a group of many jars of what some might consider rather dull-looking preserved fish. But when, for example, I examine a faded specimen labeled "*Paraluteres prionurus,* large reef, NW side of Kayangel, September 4, 1949," I can recall a pufferlike fish of brilliant colors, darting among large mushroom-shaped corals, and I remember the chase after this evasive filefish, the excited feeling when my spear finally made its mark—the capture of a souvenir from an enchanting South Sea island nine thousand miles away.

I've been asked a number of times if, when traveling alone around the Pacific islands and other remote places, I haven't run into any "difficulties" with men. Once after I gave a lecture on my Pacific trip, a woman actually asked if I carried some weapon to protect or spare me from that fate worse than death. Another time I jokingly told some people (who wondered how I took care of myself) that I was a judo expert and used this means to handle men—and they took me seriously! Perhaps I've just been lucky but I can't help believing that a man in his right mind (whether he be a South Sea islander, sailor in the U.S. Navy, or any stranger) respects a woman who does not invite trouble and who makes it clear she is just trying to do her work. My worst and practically only encounter with a "fresh fellow" is hardly worth mentioning but I'll tell you about it briefly as an example of the most unpleasant situation of its kind that I've got into during these trips.

It was on a collecting trip to a somewhat out of the way place on a Pacific island—never mind which one. Although I was perfectly willing and unafraid to go alone, it was decided by the Navy officials that a reliable Mr. "X" should go along to protect me from the natives.

I got along fine with the natives and went fish collecting with them out in shallow water while Mr. X, who wouldn't join us, sat in the hot sun and got very bored. Some men came along and invited him to join them in a thirst quencher and they produced several precious bottles. By the time I finished fishing, Mr. X was red-eyed, unsteady, and aggressive but I outran him. The native fishermen were still nearby and they gave me all the protection I needed. Mr. X sobered up quickly after a sudden "bath" in sea water. And when he was in his right mind again, he was a gentleman.

14

Off to Egypt

In 1950, as my research project in the Department of Animal Behavior was drawing to a close, I heard that under the Fulbright Bill, students, professors, and research scholars were being sent to various countries all over the world to pursue their specialized studies. Egypt was listed among these countries.

I had just read an account of the strange relationship between a little clown fish and the paralyzing sea anemone among whose tentacles he lives. The study had been made at a marine laboratory on the Egyptian coast of the Red Sea by the Director, Dr. H. A. F. Gohar Bey. I hadn't known there were facilities for marine research there. And, as I read about the Egyptian clown fish, the remarkable resemblance of the Red Sea to the tropical Pacific stood out in my mind.

The little brown-and-orange-striped fish pictured in Dr. Gohar's article was the same kind that I had seen among the coral reefs in Micronesia. Every time I spotted this pretty fish and swam closer, it would lead me to a pale pink or lavender sea anemone that looked like a chrysanthemum in the coralline gardens. A large anemone sometimes harbored several of these

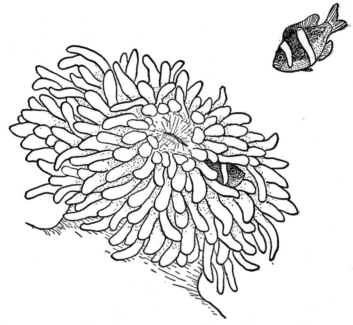

SEA ANEMONE AND CLOWN FISH

clown fish, who darted in and out of its tentacles like bees seeking honey in a giant marine flower. But if I went very close to these commensal animals, the fish snuggled deep into the tentacles of their host and remained there quietly. In that haven the clown fish were secure from their natural enemies who would be led into and paralyzed by the anemone—but they were a pitifully easy target for spearfishermen.

So these same clown fish and anemones lived in the Red Sea! Then I remembered that many of the tropical Pacific plectognaths had originally been described by early German ichthyologists who had made collections of fishes from the Red Sea. I started reading more about this sea and its lone Marine Biological Station. I learned to my surprise that practically no scientific reports had been made on the fishes of the Red Sea in over seventy years and the museums in our country had no representative collections from this area. Dr. Gohar's work was mainly with corals, rather than fish. What a unique opportunity for modern ichthyologists if the Fulbright organization would sponsor a study of the fishes in this virgin sea! And what a chance for me to compare the Red Sea with the Pacific!

I wrote to Dr. Gohar in Egypt; the Marine Biological Station at Ghardaqa on the Red Sea offered all its facilities to visiting scientists and would welcome an American to study the fish life there. Dr. Leonard Schultz in Washington informed me that the U.S. National Museum was anxious to secure a collection of Red Sea fishes and would take care of the shipment of any I could collect. Dr. Bruce Halstead, the Director of the research program on poisonous fishes sponsored by the Navy at the School for Tropical and Preventive Medicine in California, offered to analyze in his laboratory all the samples of possibly poisonous fishes that I could obtain from the Red Sea.

I outlined a program of research work with the collection and study of Red Sea plectognaths and other poisonous fishes as the main objective. I sent my proposed plan to the Fulbright headquarters and then waited for their answer.

By this time, however, a complicating element had come into the picture.

ILIAS THEMISTOKLES PAPAKONSTANTINOU had a signature that, once deciphered, made the scientific names of fishes look trivial; he also had a personality that could tempt a female ichthyologist's interests away from fish.

He was a young doctor who had shown more sincere interest in the work I was doing than any man I'd ever gone out with. He held no resentment against the odd studies that absorbed me. From him, I never heard those impatient remarks I was used to, such as, "I'm not going to play second fiddle to a fish!" Ilias had been born and raised in Greece but went to medical school in Austria. His English was colored with a quaint and amusing mixture of Greek and German accents. Like most European scholars, he could read a number of languages. He was a great help when I had to consult difficult scientific references in foreign journals and the long technical names of fishes were easy Greek to him.

There were evenings, when I was pressed for time, when our "date" consisted of translating a German ichthyological article or my calling out numbers to him and his running a calculating machine while we figured out the data on my experimental work at the Department of Animal Behavior. The museum's night watchman, making his rounds in the small hours of the morning, would shake his head at us, "In my days we'd go out dancing or to the movies. . . ." And so I couldn't complain on other evenings when I spent the whole time waiting in the lobby of St. Clare's Hospital. "This appendectomy will only take twenty minutes," Ilias said one evening when an emergency case came in; and then, three hours later, "Can you imagine, Genielein, we found an old bullet in his intestine!"

My plans to go to Egypt for a year brought things to a head —but not quite the way I expected. My Fulbright scholarship came through but Ilias was very happy when I told him the news. "That sounds terrific—studying fish in the Red Sea! And you'll be able to stop off and visit my parents in Athens."

I arrived in Cairo on Christmas Eve, 1950. Two weeks later, I saw for the first time what was to be my home for the next year—the charming little Marine Biological Station at Ghardaqa, an isolated spot at the eastern edge of the Libyan Desert where the great stretches of barren sands come to an abrupt end and are met by the blue of the Red Sea.

15

Marine Station in the Desert

I craned my neck and gazed upward at a creature standing eleven feet tall. Its face had a peculiarly blank look. The tiny eyes, set far back on the sides of its head, could hardly be seen without close examination. The forearms resembled flippers externally (although its skeletal anatomy indicated the degeneration of ancestral "fingers") and under each was a large teat that seemed more than adequate for suckling its young. The bulky smooth body tapered toward the rear into a good-sized tail fin—more like the fluke of a whale. Its head was bald and the only noticeable hairs were in the form of bristly whiskers around the mouth.

"That," said Dr. Gohar, "is the mermaid. People thought mermaids were extinct in the Red Sea until we started catching them in our nets." His blue eyes twinkled but his graying brown beard was solemn.

What we were looking at, in the little museum of the Marine Station, was a gigantic female dugong sometimes called "sea cow" or "mermaid." Dr. Gohar preferred the latter name because he liked to fill his visitors' minds with a romantic and beautiful vision beforehand and then startle them when he finally displayed the unattractive monster.

If this strange creature gave rise to the mermaid legend, as Dr. Gohar thinks likely, the sailors who first saw it must have been away from home a long time. But under certain conditions it must suggest a bit of femininity,, for even its Arabic name, *arus el bahr,* means "bride of the sea." If it is one of the largest and most startling of the Red Sea inhabitants, however, it is only one of hundreds that are equally fascinating.

The Red Sea is unique among seas. It is the northwest extreme, the upturned tail, of the great Indo-Pacific tropical waters. It differs sharply from the Mediterranean with which it is artificially connected by the thin thread of the Suez Canal. This link has made possible a small exchange of the most adaptable species between the two seas. The exchange is greatly limited, however, by the vastly different conditions that exist in the temperate Mediterranean and the tropical Red Sea and the muddy brine lakes in the canal itself form a further ecological barrier.

If you compare a typical sample of fishes from the Mediterranean with a sample from the Red Sea, the most casual eye can tell there is a great difference between them even though less than one hundred miles separate the waters from which they come. But compare a sample of fishes from Ghardaqa with a sample from Hawaii—twelve thousand miles away (as the bee flies, not as the fish swims!) and you will find such similarities that it needs expert scrutiny to detect the real differences. For the blenny that skips around the tide pools of Hawaii does the same along the Red Sea; the commonest poisonous pufferfish in Hawaii offers the same danger in the Red Sea.

However, close study does reveal that evolutionary processes are causing specializations in the comparatively isolated life in the Red Sea. These specializations have taken place over the many thousands of years this sea has been almost cut off from its mother, the Indian Ocean, the only apron string is the Strait of Bab el Mandeb, a shallow sill only 300 feet deep at the southern tip of the Red Sea.

Almost ten per cent of the species of fish found in the Red Sea are probably indigenous to it. Another large per cent shows the intermediate stages in the evolution of Indo-Pacific forms into those peculiar to the Red Sea and its special ecological conditions. Located in the midst of an arid climate where the evaporation from the water surface greatly exceeds the small rainfall, it is a great "salt basin" of exceptionally high temperature and high salinity. Unlike most seas, no rivers flow into it. Although the general depth outside the reef-bound coastal waters is about 2,200 feet, the jagged subterrane may sink more than 6,600 feet. And in these strange submarine valleys the temperature is unbelievably warm in contrast to other seas where zones of such depth are very cold.

The Red Sea, with its conveniently limited fauna and peculiar ecology, its dynamic changes and mutations, is a challenge to the marine biologist. It has been relatively neglected by modern field biologists. The Marine Biological Station at Ghardaqa, which welcomes scientists from all over the world, offers these opportunities.

The Station is actually some four miles north of the village of Ghardaqa. An office building, library, museum, engine house, and cottages for visiting scientists and the permanent staff families are spread out over the desert, forming a little community all its own.

The part of the Station that completely charms every visitor is situated at the end of a pier that extends out over the brim of the Red Sea basin. Here are compact small laboratories with many glass and stone aquaria for keeping live specimens. In one aquarium a clown fish hiding in a giant sea anemone comes out to lure another fish into the deadly tentacles of its host, where only the clown fish and a special black damsel fish are safe. In another aquarium a group of sessile anemones seem suddenly to get up and walk away; but then you can see they are only riding the shell of a hermit crab, repaying him for the transportation and stray bits from his meals by providing him with a bouquetlike camouflage. In another corner the pulsating heads of a group of xeniid soft corals move short tentacles on long stems, like a hundred arms reaching up, opening and closing their finger tips. A chicken fish with its "plumes" spread like a peacock's tail swims slowly; only when you touch it can you feel the tips of the hidden hypodermic spines of this venomous scorpion of the sea. A goby looks at you from under a piece of stone; on this stone crawls a beautiful, rosy-red mass of jelly with a ring of delicate white feathers on one end. If you pick it up and stroke the soft mass in your hands, it opens up like the circular skirt of a dancer. And then if you put it back into the water—the skirt begins to dance! With graceful undulating movements, it swims through the water as if worn by an invisible ballerina. Is it any wonder that the natives call this sea slug "Bedia" after Egypt's most famous dancer?

If you sit down at a microscope you can see the thousands of trochophore larvae twirling in little capsules taken from a pink ribbon rosette that Bedia laid on the side of her aquarium last week. But if you look up from your microscope and out the window, your attention will be drawn to a monstrous manta ray, a half dozen nurse sharks, a sawfish with a double-edged "saw" longer than your arm, sting rays, guitar fish, and a hundred other fantastic marine animals living in the large outdoor pools beside the laboratories.

If you like swimming, you can dive off the end of the pier into the clear blue open sea, adjust your face mask, and in a few strokes find yourself in an infinite aquarium scintillating with strange and beautiful marine animals peering at you from sanctuaries in a large coral garden.

This was my workshop.

Living quarters at the Marine Station were more than comfortable. There were two cottages for visiting scientists, with space for twelve people if necessary. But as there were seldom more than two or three scientists there at a time, I usually had a place all to myself.

My cottage bordered the edge of the desert on one side and the Red Sea lapped under the other. At high tide I could just reach my quarters and still keep my feet dry. From the back balcony I could look over the sea—like an ocean on some days, like a still lake on others—to the mountains on the southern tip of the Sinai peninsula in the clear distance. From the front porch, desert plains and mountains composed the scenery. Nearby was a pink-and-white-striped building, the native's mosque. From my window I saw the worshipers come down to the sea and wash themselves before going in to the mosque to pray. And then I could hear the voice of the muezzin and the chanting of the passages from the Koran. Sometimes in the evening the children from nearby homes beat out a characteristic rhythm on homemade drums. They sang and danced, and the exotic quarter-tone music of the Arabs came clearly across the desert from Soliman the Sailor's flute—an incredibly sweet-toned instrument which consisted merely of eight holes drilled in a lead pipe.

Dr. Gohar was at the Station during my first two weeks there. Most of the remaining time, however, he was away— usually in Cairo where he was professor at Fouad University of which the Station is a part. Before leaving he acquainted me with all the facilities of the Station, introduced me to the men who would help me to get the fishes I was after, and in general

was of invaluable help in getting me started. Much of the time
he spent teaching me Arabic.

The French I'd learned at school helped a little in Cairo,
but here on the Red Sea, the people I had to deal with—
the fishermen, sailors, and divers—spoke only Arabic. And not
the ordinary Arabic, but a dialect peculiar to the regions of
Upper Egypt and the Red Sea coast. Hard G's were stuck in
words where dictionaries didn't give them; hence the first
Arabic word I learned in Cairo, *ahwa* (coffee), was pronounced
gahwa at the Red Sea and little cups of black *gahwa* (slightly
sweet, very sweet, or just right) were served as often in
Ghardaqa as *ahwa* was in Cairo—at the drop of a tarbush,
whenever there was an excuse for a few minutes' break in a
long hot day. A fish upside down in a bottle was *maglub* not
malub. The official name of the Marine Biological Station was
Mohatta el ahyaa el baharya but I soon learned that when
its Director was not within hearing distance it was called
Mohatta abu dign (Station with a beard)—but not because
of the peculiarity of the local dialect.

Arabic writing intrigued me. I was used to writing from left
to right, even from top to bottom in Japanese classes, but
Arabic's right to left was a novelty I delighted in learning.
Arabic writing is like a beautiful design and indeed it is used
as such in the decorations of mosques. I'd studied the alphabet
and started putting some of the artistic combinations together
in Cairo, feeling it might give me a headstart at Ghardaqa.
But alas, none of the men I was to work with at sea could

read or write or appreciate my efforts to learn their written language.

Before Dr. Gohar left, I wrote down all the expressions I thought might come in handy; after that I was on my own.

Every day started off with my saying "Good morning" in Arabic to every person I met: my houseboy, the cook, the sailors, and whoever else might be around. This unladylike expression, which sounds like clearing your throat, gave me much practice with the guttural "H" of the Arabic language.

As time went on, I found it was easy to get along with the natives. They come from a mixture of backgrounds: fishermen and farmers from the Nile Valley, Negroes from the Sudan, Arabs from the desert. They were all kind to me. The fishermen particularly were very helpful—patiently trying to follow my broken Arabic instructions, teaching me the new words I groped for, repeating them with emphasis so that I could get the proper pronunciation in a tactful and casual way that never sounded as though they were correcting me.

My houseboy, Shehat, and the cook, Mohammed, treated me like a pampered daughter. I was free to devote all my time to my work with fish as they did everything else for me. Shehat once scolded me when he caught me rinsing out a pair of my socks. "In the name of Allah, what are you doing? You may know about the fish in the sea, but what do you know of washing socks? See the dirt you have left on their bottoms! I always wash them so clean. Isn't my way good enough for you? Allah knows I try my best to please you . . ." or words to that effect. On and on he went as though I had wounded him deeply.

Shehat made sure I realized he was doing a good job of taking care of my cottage. When he cleaned my room he also killed the flies. When there were many, he neatly piled the corpses in a conspicuous place and left them there until he was sure I had seen them. I wasn't keen on this gesture. For one thing it sometimes attracted other and worse insects. But I pretended not to notice the neat piles and neither complimented Shehat as he was expecting nor reprimanded him as I sometimes wanted to do. It didn't happen too often. The region of Ghardaqa, even in summer, is kept surprisingly comfortable by frequent breezes that also keep the flies from being too numerous.

One exceptionally hot and breezeless day, however, I was trying to work in my lab dissecting and preserving a fresh catch of fish. The flies were thick about us, some even had the nerve to ride the blade of my scalpel as I cut into the abdomens of my specimens to examine their viscera. I could picture Shehat back at the cottage engaged in one of his favorite occupations.

I decided to make my own collection of dead flies—not quite a fair one, I must admit. Some I swatted but others I picked out of a pan of formalin where a half-preserved fish had lured them to their death. At the end of the afternoon I went home to take a shower and brought my fly collection with me. Shehat's catch for the day was in its usual place. I put my pile carefully next to his. Mine had more flies in it. That evening after supper when I returned to my room, both piles had been removed. Shehat stopped by later to say his usual good night. This time, however, he ceremoniously made a low bow with his hand over his heart and said with a serious expression, "Allah knows the *doctora* is a better flycatcher than Shehat." Then he looked up slyly and we both laughed. After that he no longer left his insect catches around for me to appraise.

When Shehat came along on fishing trips, he insisted on acting like a valet, rushing over with a dry towel as soon as I came out of the water. He watched me like an anxious mother hen when I made a deep dive or sharks were around. He wailed and wiped his dry eyes the day I left. He knew little about the sea. Shehat never came on our long boat trips as he got seasick, but these trips were Mohammed's greatest pleasure.

The Station had only sailboats. To reach the outer reefs took a good two hours' sail over the beautiful sea. No matter how rough the sailing, Mohammed always served a hot cup of *gahwa* on the way. On long trips he could whip up a full course meal in the tiny hull space below the deck. Mohammed was an expert sailor on his own, but he was officially the cook on these trips, and when he wasn't at his job, he either sat and smoked his homemade hubble-bubble pipe (with a built-in beer can to hold the water) or mended his own nets, brought along to pass the time. But he was a valuable man. He could prepare fish of all kinds in every conceivable manner. He knew how to serve mermaids, octopi, sea turtles, the giant clam, and everything else edible that we brought out of the sea for him. He knew how to make European as well as Egyptian dishes, and with a little training, learned something of Japanese cookery when my stepfather sent me a package with the essential seasonings. The only dish he had difficulty with was raw fish. When he had the slices placed on the plate and ready to serve as I'd instructed him, he'd still ask me to come to the kitchen first and check to see if he hadn't forgotten to do something more with the fish.

During one of Dr. Gohar's stays at the Station, I told Mohammed to prepare a Japanese-style meal. For the occasion I gave Mohammed my new sets of ivory chopsticks that I had had especially made in Cairo, with tiny fish carved on the handle ends. But when Dr. Gohar and I sat down to the table, the chopsticks had not been set out. When Mohammed came in bearing the tray with the first course, I made a motion to him inquiring about the chopsticks. He smiled at me with that you-didn't-think-I'd-forget look on his face and lifted the cover off the plate on his tray in which sat the first course—the chopsticks.

Mohammed, Shehat, and the other men who worked at the Station lived nearby with their families. Their children were always out playing and screamed with laughter when I spoke my broken Arabic to them. They were the surest subjects on which to test my Arabic. They were never so polite as to pretend to understand me if they didn't.

The first few weeks I seldom saw the women, and when I did, they were heavily veiled and looked mysterious. But as time went on, they became used to the idea of an American woman who wore a bathing suit and went fishing with their

men, and instead of turning away, they started answering my
greetings. In the privacy of their homes, they liked to have
their pictures taken, which I did for them several times. When
I visited them, they let down their veils and were as chummy
and nice as women anywhere. They liked to shower me with
their perfumes and for days afterward you could smell I'd been
visiting.

An ichthyologist in a strange land has everything in his favor.
There is a natural urge in all peoples to help out a stranger—
whether it springs from a sincere desire to help, an impulse
to show off, or merely curiosity to get one's nose in closer.
And when you're a stranger who's come to hunt and study
fishes—whether you stop for a day on a remote South Sea
island (where you don't know a word of the local tongue) or
come for a year to the end of the desert (where you gradually learn to stumble through sentences) you will be surprised
at the eagerness of the local Isaak Waltons to help you get the
fish you want most.

You may not receive a warm response if you ask a rich
friend to help you obtain money, but ask a strange fisherman
to help you find a specific fish (the harder and rarer the better)
and you will immediately get his interest and eventually his
wholehearted help. You don't have to know his language; just
draw a picture of the fish, gesticulate for his help, and let him
lead the way. In doing so you have told him three important
things: you have not come just to stare at him and his people,
you have a specific interest in common with his; you respect

his judgment and recognize his superior knowledge of local conditions (and a native fisherman knows more about his water than the most highly trained ichthyologist); and you trust him.

Sharing the fun of fishing turns strangers into friends in a few hours. Whether you sit with native fishermen in their boat and fish with nets and lines or dive under the sea with them—they will lead you to the haunts of the specimens you desire and you could not find yourself in safer and more enjoyable company.

16

Fishing in the Red Sea

"Oh, to be like a pipefish!" might well be the exclamation of a pregnant woman with an unsympathetic husband.

Pipefish, those sticklike elongated relatives of the sea horse, form with the latter a small group of animals which have a unique distinction among all living creatures. It's the male who has the babies.

I had my first chance to study "pregnant" male pipefish after trawling over beds of sea grass in a shallow, sandy-bottom area of the Red Sea just north of the Marine Biological Station. We started early in the morning. The sun wasn't yet high enough to be warming but the wind was—high enough, that is, to be chilling as our small sailboat zig-zagged through the choppy sea and sprays of water hit us, evaporating quickly in the wind and leaving the flesh salty and cold. Shivering under a heavy sweater and slacks, I recalled the comments of friends when they heard I was going to the Red Sea. "The heat there is awful—unbearable! A whole year? You'll be sorry!" My only regret, I should like to tell these people, is that I didn't bring warmer clothes with me. Those early mornings, and evenings after the sun went down, except for the few mid-summer months, were far from warm.

Soliman the Sailor, to distinguish him from four other Solimans who worked at the Station, was the brother of our cook, Mohammed. Soliman was a good sailor to be sure. On a calm day he might hold the rudder stick with his foot and play on his lead pipe, squinting in the strong reflected sunlight until his small grey eyes almost disappeared behind the high cheekbones of his finely chiseled Arab face. But on these January mornings when we first trawled, he controlled the rudder stick with a strong arm and called out directions for changing the high white sail to the other two men who were with us.

It took skillful maneuvering to tack into the wind while avoiding the numerous jagged reefs that cluttered our path to the sea grass beds. The sail had to be turned a number of times before we got there. It was a fast hectic operation each time the sail was turned. I would duck low in the place they indicated for me as the two sailors rushed around in their bare feet over the slippery wet deck, untying ropes and swinging the sail—the boat tipped way over at an angle where I could see in detail the beautiful but menacing reef each time we turned. How, during this mad rush, the men missed knocking off their bulky turbans or tripping over the long clumsy skirts of their galabias, was beyond me.

Even when we reached the trawling area, their job was far from easy. In order to bring up delicate specimens—such as the translucent pink razorfish that looks like a blade of grass and always swims standing on its head—alive or at least in good condition for preserving, the trawl had to be dragged behind the boat at a slow steady speed and pulled up after a limit of ten minutes. The large heavy trawl net had to be carefully lifted onto the boat and emptied into a tub of sea water, where keen eyes and cautious quick fingers sorted the specimens from the debris of the grass beds that constituted the bulk of the catch. The grass often contained sharp-clawed crabs, prickly sea urchins with brittle spines that break off after sliding under your skin, small pufferfish with strong beak-like dentures that snap onto careless fingers, several varieties of well-camouflaged fishes with sharp poisonous spines, and various kinds of in-vertebrates whose jellylike and slimy bodies were stinging to the touch. And a novice could easily get his fingers harmlessly but uncomfortably entangled with writhing octopus legs or, worse still, the adhesive threads extruded from the sea cu-cumber or "penis of the sea" as the Arab seamen call this animal because of superficial resemblances such as its shape, its habit of becoming turgid when handled, and the manner in which it often shoots out a clear stream of water and, on rarer occasions, a milky substance.

In an hour's trawling we could get as many as thirty different kinds of fish from the grass beds. Filefishes were among the most common, fortunately for me, because I wanted to collect a large series to prove some differences between the males and females that could not be shown from just a few specimens. A very rare fish, *Solenostomus*, meaning the pipe-mouthed (I know of no common name for it), is seldom seen alive by man. But we caught several in our trawl and brought them back to the lab where we could observe them in the aquarium. Some were almost all white, some almost all black, and some pinkish with black spots—depending on the color of the weeds in which they were caught. And they moved little more than the plants they resembled.

The pipefish and sea horses were for me the most amusing specimens in our trawl catches. Back in the aquarium they could be watched closely. They looked so unfishlike. They seldom swam about but when they did it was in slow motion; they moved like phantoms for the tiny fins that propelled them by rapid twirling were practically invisible. Usually they clung to plants by curling their prehensile tails around stems, their bodies held upright. The sea horses had their heads pulled in like shy maidens; the pipefish, without such a "neck" joint development, held their long heads in line with their bodies, snouts high in the water as if snubbing all creatures around them. Once I saw this appearance of a pipefish brought down a peg or two. A demure sea horse with its head bowed gracefully swam slowly by the stuck-up head of a motionless pipefish who looked for all the world like another branch of the plant to which he'd attached himself. The sea horse, deciding that this protruding proboscis would make a convenient holdfast, gently wrapped his tail around it. The two fish, linked together in this pose, seemed like the circus elephants of the marine world.

The "lips" around the small mouth at the end of the elongated snout of some sea horses and pipefish turn out as if in a pout—so apropos an expression on the males during the gestation period when their bellies are swollen with developing

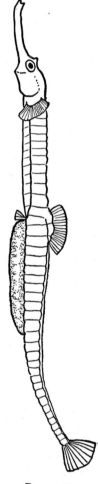

PREGNANT
MALE
PIPEFISH

embryos! Such an incongruity in this Man's World! The females, having deposited their eggs in the males long before (the male fertilizes the eggs after they are in his body), are free of maternal duties. The male is left with the responsibility of bringing the babies into the world. I never happened to witness the birth process but some writers who have, report that male sea horses actually appear to have "labor pains."

At low tide some of the coral reefs off shore were almost exposed. You could walk across them in water no higher than your knees. On calm days the sea was like a sheet of glass and you could look down into the colorful busy world of those marine fairylands.

On such days I went out with just one or two sailors in a dugout canoe, on which a small sail could be rigged if a breeze came up. We could paddle quickly and directly to the reef we wanted to explore. The canoe slipped over the shallowest reefs along the way. Only on rare occasions did we have to get out and wade across a reef and pull the canoe behind us.

The corals that compose these reefs were as sharp as they were beautiful. The men wore old shoes on these excursions. I had a pair of old sneakers but still had to watch my step, for the toxic spines of purple sea urchins could penetrate right through the canvas uppers.

Although miles of reefs were around us, we often spent the whole morning in a small area of a few square yards just poking about, picking up small chunks of reef, shaking out small fishes, crabs, marine worms, octopi, shellfish and sea slugs, and examining the coral surfaces for egg deposits left by the hundreds of kinds of creatures whose young emerge from coralline crevices. Then, back in the lab with our collection of living reef treasures, a whole afternoon would fly by. Hours went in studying just one tiny cluster of white beads, each half the size of a lemon pit, in which squid embryos bounced up and down from the pulsations of their miniature jet-propulsion systems—the opening and closing of the exhaust outlets clearly visible through the microscope.

The sea slugs we picked off the corals obligingly laid their eggs in the lab, often against the side wall of a glass aquarium. I could sit with a magnifying glass and watch the details as the slow spiraling creature left a band of eggs. The egg bands of some species were in the form of a tightly coiled watch spring. But the precision machine that constructed this band was a lowly animal that usually crawls about willy-nilly as if it never had much of an idea where it was going.

These shell-less relatives of snails, which vary from the size

of a small fingernail to the giant "glamour girl" slug of the
Red Sea, *Bedia*, whose unfurled crimson skirt may measure a
foot across, are more correctly called nudibranchs. This name
refers to their "naked gills" which, when the animal is undisturbed, protrude from the back like a ring of fragile waving
feathers, stirring the water and absorbing precious oxygen. On
the head end of these nudibranchs you can usually see two
tentacles or feelers which move about in all directions as its
owner slithers over the corals and stones, but which are quickly
withdrawn when the creature is disturbed and comes to an
abrupt halt. I much prefer the name "nudibranch" to "sea slug"
for these animals. The word "slug" suggests a small, dull gray
animal crawling among rotting debris. Nudibranchs are among
the most gorgeous and exquisitely colored creatures that live on
the reefs. Small wonder the Emperor of Japan collects them as
a hobby. From an aesthetic point of view there is no comparison
between Red Sea nudibranchs and true slugs, which incidentally
lack the exposed gill structure of the former.

From above, you usually see only the mantle of a nudibranch
which often resembles a skirt with ruffles around the edge. It
is smooth and jellylike and undulates in the water to propel the
animal on the rare occasions when it swims. Near the front
end of the mantle are the feelers and toward the rear, the waving gills like plumes on a lady's hat. We collected a dozen
different nudibranchs. A painter, using his most brilliant colors
and composing the most exquisite designs with them, would
have difficulty rivaling the mantles of these nudibranchs.
One had a design of anastomosing stripes of gold alternating

with peacock-blue and its gills and feelers were golden. Another had a delicate yellow net design down the center of a chalk-white mantle with a rich purple band edging the "ruffle" and fine purple rings around its feelers. Another had a ruffle of black and pale emerald. And you already know the spectacular *Bedia*.

Under the mantle is a firm muscular structure called the "foot." Like the foot of a snail, it is the locomotor organ of the animal when it crawls over the substratum. When a nudibranch crawls up the side of a glass aquarium, you can study the under side of the mantle and the foot structure. On one side of the foot is a small opening from which you can see the egg mass extruded, if you are lucky enough to catch this process. It is then especially that you are apt to refer to this gaudily painted, delicate creature you are watching as a "she." But it is from this position that you can most readily observe another structure that occasionally extends from under the mantle—a large penis which betrays the hermaphroditic nature of this strange, otherwise feminine creature of the sea.

There is a funny way of making a big collection of big reef fishes. A casual onlooker might have thought we were playing some child's game when the fisherman and I, led by Soliman the Sailor, suddenly burst into a wild dance over the reef, shouting, splashing, throwing rocks, and hitting sticks in the water. But the seemingly helter-skelter frenzied action is the climax of a careful plan of attack and each of us has a specific part in a pattern of movement that constitutes one of the most effective fishing methods of Arab reef fishermen.

It begins by stalking the prey—quietly, cautiously, from a distance. Our sailboat approaches a large reef and the sailors look it over until they spot a shallow area where ripples stir the surface of an otherwise still sea. Here the tips of tails of many large fishes—bending down, chewing, and breaking into the corals to feed on the tiny crabs, worms, and other delicacies living inside—break the surface of the water. These fishes usually swim along the outer edge of the reef in the protection of deep water where they are hard to catch in groups and have to be hooked or speared individually. But when they come up onto the shallow reef to feed this way—we have a chance for a truly big catch.

And so we slowly lower the anchor of our boat a good distance away. There must be no splash or strong vibration made in the water. Our canoe, with the long nets and other equipment ready in it, is untied from the sailboat and we get in and paddle slowly, softly, mostly gliding until we reach the edge of the reef. Here we slip into the water and move noiselessly, spreading a long double net of two mesh sizes along the edge of the reef. The width of the net is about three feet between the sinkers and the floats—more than the depth of the water at this point. The net's length of some sixty feet is unfolded completely until it forms a semicircle around the feeding fishes. The fishes, however, are already aware that something is going on and few tail tips are breaking the surface now.

This is the moment for the big scare that will send them in

the right direction. Three or four of us have by now worked our way around to the other side of the group of tensing fish and the commotion starts. The two men holding the ends of the net run toward each other. The rest of us come in closing the circle and the long silence is suddenly broken by our noisy splashing and shouting. The excited and frightened mass of fish rush about, most of them heading directly for the deep water at the edge of the reef where they become entangled between the two layers of our net. A small number try to escape in our direction—and indeed a few get through our line, slapping our legs with their strong bodies as they slip past us. And although we must try to keep our legs in their way and make enough disturbance so they will turn around and go toward the net, we must also be careful to avoid the tails of the large surgeon fish whose sharp "knives" are now extended to gash the enemy who gets in the way of their escape.

When the excitement is over it is rewarding to examine the net. Sometimes it has caught over a hundred food fishes—mostly large parrot fish, rabbit fish, and surgeon fish but with a variety of other large reef fishes that were also feeding among these schools—snappers, grunts, pufferfish, triggerfish, boxfish, perhaps even a sting ray. By weight, this was the most successful way to catch reef fishes.

Unlike the Arab fishermen, however, the bulk of my collection was not as important as the variety of species and a two-ounce fish might be more valuable to me than a twenty-pound one. I was interested in obtaining as many types of Red

Sea fishes as possible and in trying to find new kinds never reported from this sea before. The standard method of poisoning, used by ichthyologists, was still the most effective for this purpose.

There aren't many good places with tide pool formations along the Red Sea coast in the areas I investigated. And the difference between high and low tides is not as marked there as in most sea coasts of the world. Several times we tried poisoning some open reefs with excellent results. In one spot on the island of Shadwan we obtained ninety-eight different species of fishes—among them many of the rarest kinds known from the Red Sea, and several never found in this sea before. But we had to use great quantities of my limited supply of the rotenone poison.

The tide pools we poisoned took very small amounts of rotenone to capture all the piscine gems they harbored. The natives were intrigued with this method that they had never seen used before.

Because we could drive along the coast to reach the tide pools, instead of going to our fishing grounds by boat, weak-stomached Shehat always came along. He loved this method of fishing where he could merely stoop over in ankle-deep water and with two fingers gingerly pick up a floating dead fish by its tail. In the time one of the other men gathered dozens of fish, Shehat would prance his way over the reefs to bring me his single specimen and ask if it was a new species.

The centers of these pools were often quite deep. I wore sneakers, my bathing suit, and used my face mask to search the bottom and deep crevices where the grogged fish sometimes lodged themselves. The men, too, wearing their knee-length shorts waded into the deeper water to retrieve the fish—all except Shehat, this is. He meandered around the rim of the tide pool where the water was shallowest, holding the skirt hem of his neat purple galabia between his teeth, bending over and giggling with delight and surprise at all the creatures of the tide pool world that came floundering out of their hiding places as the rotenone did its job. He wouldn't touch anything he didn't recognize as a fish, but he came to realize that some very unfishlike objects were classified as fish and was always hoping to find some new kind. He would keep calling the other men over whenever he spotted something he thought was unusual.

"Come here quickly. See what I've found—a creature Allah himself may not know about! Take it immediately to the *doctora* and be sure to tell her I discovered it."

"Landsman, stop bothering us and pick it up yourself. That's only a common sea worm," a fisherman might tell him. They finally sent him off screaming by dropping crabs in the folds of his galabia skirt and tossing at him serpentine starfish with long wriggling arms.

Once when we started collecting in a tide pool, Shehat disappeared for a short time and when he reappeared he was walking proudly with his head high and wearing a *bathing suit*. It was one of those old-fashioned, one-piece men's suit covering most of the chest and with a low waistline and short skirt—the kind that went out of style forty years ago. I don't know where he got it but it had evidently first belonged to a man twice the width of lean Shehat. The sight stopped us from our work and we all gaped at him, hardly able to believe our eyes. Soliman murmured something in Arabic I didn't understand but it had the tone of "Get a load o' that, will ya!" As all eyes followed him, Shehat headed for the open sea. He was less confident now as he glanced from the corner of his eye to see our reactions. Then the men started on him.

"Shehat, where are you going in that outfit? You can't swim!"

"If you go into the water you'll attract every shark in the sea. But don't worry, when they get a good look at you they'll all run away!"

"Did you send to Cairo for that sea suit? Surely such elegant outfits can't be bought at Qena."

"Be sure to change your clothes before you say your prayers or Allah won't recognize you as a Muslum."

Comments like these, along with much cruder ones, were hurled at Shehat who suddenly became as shy as a girl caught in her slip. He ran back to our truck parked in the desert, his arms crossed over his chest and hands clinging to his shoulders and we never saw him in a bathing suit again.

Gomah was the cleverest of the sailors; he was also a clown. He had a lisp. The absence of his upper front teeth formed an opening from which he often sprayed the other sailors' faces, accidentally or otherwise, when he talked excitedly. He was husky and strong but quite short. Abdullah, the gigantic Sudanese who was Dr. Gohar's chauffeur, loved to put an arm around Gomah and hug the short fellow's head against his ribs until Gomah's turban cocked to one side—then Gomah would stagger away, pretending to be crushed to dizziness.

Gomah made a funny little figure even when he wasn't trying. He and the Station's carpenter lived in adjacent houses. At the work day's end they usually walked home together, holding hands and swinging their arms, their long shadows exaggerating this movement. They looked to me like a pair of young school-girls in this walking habit which is common among Arab men and no reflection on their masculinity. Gomah and the carpenter would chatter to each other simultaneously, recounting the highlights and their complaints of the day, neither listening to the other but both getting things off their chests to a good friend —things that would be of no significance by the next day any-how.

Gomah would not be outdone by an American girl doing back flips off a boat. One late afternoon, after regular hours, I heard some laughter from the end of the pier and looked out of my lab window. Several men were standing on the pier, a little boy was holding Gomah's turban and galabia, and Gomah was repeatedly throwing himself backward off the pier, landing on his bald head, his stumpy, wide-spread, bent-kneed legs slapping the water in a resounding splash. But he did not give up. After numerous attempts, he finally redonned his turban triumphantly and slipped his galabia over his reddened skin. But he had mastered the back flip so that he hit the water feet first, even if the rest of his form was a bit unorthodox.

Gomah and Atiyah were my "spearfishermen" at the Red Sea. They tried their best but could hardly compare with the spear-fishermen of the South Pacific. Gomah outdid himself if he dived down fifteen feet. And how Atiyah managed to spear the many fine fish he did I never knew. He couldn't count the fingers held up to him at two arms' length. He had a reputation as a spearfisherman, and indeed his aim was accurate. But he couldn't spear a specific fish I might spot and want very much. He simply couldn't see what I was pointing at. However, he had developed some remarkable system for spearing a blurred moving object in the water and he caught some excellent specimens that way. It was claimed that he could dive to seventy feet—but he never gave me a demonstration. As far as I could surmise, neither he nor Gomah especially liked getting their heads under water. They preferred to spear fish by walking along the edge of the reef, in water not above their armpits, holding a long, all-metal spear in one hand and looking through a glass-bottomed box directed with the other.

It is strange, but among all the Red Sea fishermen I met, I never saw or heard of one who used even the most primitive type of underwater goggles—a device tropical Pacific fishermen consider essential these days. Pacific divers may dive without clothes, without weapons of any kind except their hands and teeth, but they always have goggles.

After much coaxing, I finally got Gomah to try a face mask. At first he complained, something to the effect that it's a wonderful gadget but the water leaks in and the glass gets cloudy and if it were possible to spear fish underwater with one's eyes closed, he wouldn't mind wearing the mask at all. But then he learned to adjust the mask properly and breathe in through his nose a little to make a vacuum and the mask stopped leaking. However, I think I sold him the idea when I explained that the glass of the mask would not get foggy if a thin layer of saliva was smeared on it. Gomah could do this quickly. With his mouth and teeth clenched, he needed only to lift his upper lip slightly and a copious amount of the required liquid would hit the glass of the mask held at arm's length.

The mask opened a new world of sight to Gomah—as it had once done for me and so many other enthusiasts of the sport of underwater goggling. It's one thing to look down at the reefs through a glass-bottomed box or boat—another to be under the sea yourself, swimming freely among the reefs and seeing clearly in every direction. Gomah knew the sea well, but this method of looking at it was a new experience for him.

Going underwater goggling in the Red Sea presents a re-markably abrupt change in scenery. I recall particularly a place some thirty miles south of Ghardaqa called Sharks' Bay where this change impressed me the most. At one moment I stood on the hot sands of the barren desert; the next moment I found myself in one of the most beautiful places I have ever seen—a refreshingly cool place, a submarine coral garden of brilliant colors and teeming with life.

In Sharks' Bay the desert terrain drops suddenly beneath the sea and is transformed into a short fringing reef. My first look at this unusually gorgeous reef is still a vivid picture in my mind. The edge of the first shelf of the reef dropped down at a sharp angle to a ledge about twenty feet wide some twenty-five feet below me. This ledge in turn sloped off into a deep, richly blue water, toward a bottom I could not see. Almost every spot on the reef was overgrown with corals of the most graceful, delicate, and unusual forms. Some grew like clusters of pink and lavender flowers, others were round and solid with winding channels on their surfaces making them look like the denuded, convoluted brains of mammals—small ones like the brains of marmosets, monstrous ones that seemed to come from the heads of Goliaths. Some of the corals grew like branches of a tree or antlers of a deer, some had straight surfaces like table tops standing on a single center leg. One type of coral sat in little sandy patches on the ledge below looking exactly like the heads of yellow mushrooms. There were corals that grew in the form of large branched fans—one of these varieties I had to be careful not to touch for I knew only too well the effects of its poisonous sting. Some of the "soft" corals were in the shapes of cups, goblets, and heads of lettuce.

Sprinkled among these variegated corals were numerous other invertebrate creatures looking, as the corals did, like plants growing in a garden instead of the animals they actually are. Of these I saw vermilion sponges, sticking out of the corals like pointing fingers that had just been dipped into a can of the most brilliant red paint; the familiar sea anemones with clustered pastel tentacles harboring striped clown fish; purple plumed heads of "disappearing" worms that can recoil in a flash into the tube that hides the true, wormlike body of this otherwise lovely creature; nudibranchs crawling slowly and crabs crawling quickly.

And you could see a thousand fishes at a glance. There were dozens of varieties of small fishes, glittering sea gems that lived in close association with the corals: a school of hundreds of little

emeralds, another of rubies, and another like a band of escaped
convicts with black and white stripes on their bodies and pelvic
fins edged in sapphire. These three types of damsel fishes all
headed into branched corals when I approached them. Here they
could be captured by merely breaking off a branch of the coral
and shaking it over a small meshed net. But tiny topaz and opal
blennies crept into deeper crevices where enemies could not
reach them.

The heads of larger fishes peered out from alcoves in the
reef: yellow-and-brown-speckled sea basses, coppery squirrel
fish, black and green moray eels. Schools of whiskered, yellow
and pink goatfishes went by on the ledge below, their delicate
chin barbels feeling in the sand. Surgeon, butterfly, balloon, and
box fishes swam all about me. Big green parrot fish, keeping a
good distance away, went by eyeing me suspiciously while stopping periodically to chew off chunks of coral with their strong
"beaks" that made an audible crunching sound.

Away from the reef a large school of silvery herringlike fish
passed by with their protractile mouths held wide open as if
they'd all just yawned and their jaws had locked in that position. Delicious food fishes such as big snappers, lethrinid
scavenger fish, and fast swimming jack fish tempted the spear.
And from the deep blue depths an occasional shark came
swimming by with little regard for me.

Only the spear I held gave me any trouble. I had none of
my own and was using the Station's spears—the kind Atiyah
handled so well. But the all-metal spears used by Red Sea fishermen are not practical for underwater spearfishing. They are

too heavy and feel like an anchor after you swim with one for a few minutes. Their only advantage is that if the fish you're after is down deep, you can dive toward it with little exertion.

As I swam along Sharks' Bay reef with one of these metal spears, struggling to keep near the surface where I could take an occasional breath while looking over the seascape, I spotted a large flat fish lying in the sand on the ledge below. It was one of those easy targets. It didn't move even as I let the spear drag me down toward what I hoped was one of the poisonous sting rays I was particularly seeking. But just as I was about to thrust the spear in the fish's back, I recognized the species. It was a ray all right—an electric ray! My spear would have been a fine conductor if the fish and I had connected.

Gomah was swimming behind me, unconcerned by my near electrocution. I guess he figured that I knew what I was doing. The electric organs of this ray are located on only certain parts of its back and with careful aim I could have avoided these areas. And if I missed, the shock of an electric ray isn't enough to kill a human being. Like most dangerous sea creatures, its harmfulness to man is usually exaggerated and misinformation often leads the person unfamiliar with sea creatures to form an unfair opinion of it. A diver can swim among most "dangerous" fishes, even tickle the belly of many a shark without being bitten, but unfortunately it is always the exceptional case that makes the news.

It is as if Neptune came on land and visited one of our cities and then returned to his home and told the sea folks, "What dangers face you in the cities of land folks! Everyone must cross dozens of streets a day and down each street race hundreds of cars which can run over you and crush you to death. And many dogs are walked along these streets, vicious animals that can tear you apart with their sharp teeth and sometimes these dogs foam at the mouth and then the slightest bite causes a most horrible death."

Yes, it's true there are dangers. But let's not exaggerate them. Instead, let's define the limits of such dangers—even if it doesn't make the most spectacular account of one's experiences.

I learned that there are relatively few poisonous fishes in the Red Sea. Some thirty different kinds fall into the venomous category. Most of these are scorpion fishes and sting rays, known to cause serious cases of poisoning—but I couldn't find one report of a death from them in the Red Sea area. Several species of siganid or rabbit fish and a plotosid fish resembling a catfish have mildly venomous spines.

Among the poisonous-to-eat variety, only the pufferfishes seem to be of real danger to man and all of these are very easy to recognize. Dr. Halstead's reports from his laboratory in California indicated that all the other fish samples I sent him, which I suspected might be poisonous, were harmless.

Aside from fish, there are a number of other poisonous animals in the Red Sea. Many of these give stinging wounds, but again none are potent enough to endanger life. I was more afraid of finding a scorpion in my cottage than of meeting any of the poisonous creatures in the sea at my door.

There is an interesting case of turtle poisoning in these waters that I had not heard before. It seems to be a definite case where an animal becomes poisonous from the type of food it eats—a factor suspected in some poisonous fishes but not yet proven. This species of marine turtle is popular as native food. It is large and meaty, sometimes one may weigh a half a ton. Its food consists of fishes, sponges, soft corals, but it is particularly fond of a certain jellyfish, a stinging animal with poison cells abundant at certain seasons. Turtles feeding on these jellyfish become poisonous to eat.

However, if a turtle is kept on a poison-free diet for several days, it becomes edible. The local fishermen know this and use this curing method when a turtle is captured alive. But if the turtle dies before such treatment is possible, they cut open the animal and taste the blood from the heart. If this irritates the tongue the turtle is discarded. If the blood is nonirritating the flesh is said to be fit for eating.

It is usually the sea snake that is considered the most dangerous reptile of tropical marine waters, but none has ever been reported from the Red Sea. The many varieties of moray eels are occasionally mistaken for sea snakes and indeed morays are as dangerous in the Red Sea as any other—but of course they are not poisonous. Careless moments can occur when you suddenly catch yourself, just in time, from reaching into a moray's home in a reef hole—just as sometimes you step off a curb without looking and a car happens to race by within inches of you. But it is only logical to look where you're going and to know the dangers of your environment on land or in the sea. Once you are familiar with the sea's dangers and know where to expect them and how to avoid them, you can roam with safety and assurance in a world of wonder that otherwise you will never really know.

17

From Early Morning Till Late at Night

I was never lonely. The days were so full of things to do, I could never find time for everything. It always amused me when a visitor came to see the Marine Station and, discovering I was living alone in this remote place, took pity on me and suggested various things I might do to *kill* time!

Once or twice a week I might spend the whole day at sea. But usually I had to limit fishing trips to the mornings for there was much work to do in the lab, museum, and library in order to make the most of the trips to sea.

Sorting our collection had to be attended to almost as soon as we returned to the lab. Living specimens had to be placed in aquaria and arranged in groups that would get along together. Then they could be studied at leisure—but sometimes a fish's first reactions to its new environment reveal strange types of behavior not seen later when the fish has become used to its new home and companions. The first encounters of fish in an aquarium are particularly interesting to watch—a stage where the fish does not quite know what to expect of its new comrades. For example, among the pufferfish, there was a dull olive one that suddenly developed bright golden rings around its eyes, a fleeting flash of pigment (was it a warning to the other fish?) that he never displayed again; a small puffer that lifted a fold along the middle of its back (instead of blowing up its stomach), a reaction that reminded me of a frightened cat arching its back with hairs standing on end; and there was a big round puffer that nonchalantly swam past a tiny damsel fish for the first and only time, after which it learned to keep out of the way of this pugnacious little attacker who chewed off pieces of tail from the largest of puffers that crossed its path.

The dead fishes we collected, especially the rare ones, had to be studied quickly for their fast fading colors. Specimens not conveniently preserved in the field had to be done as soon as possible in the lab. There were dissections to be made; anatomical details of new and rare species were sketched and described. On occasions the mere sorting of our collection would continue late into the night.

I usually compared my collections with those in the Station's museum. This modest museum, under the constant interest of the Director, has accumulated what is probably the world's finest collection of animals and plants found in the Red Sea. Dr. Gohar's specialty is corals and they constituted a large part of the exhibits. The magnificently prepared specimens

of his huge assortment brought "ohs" and "ahs" from his lady
visitors who always wanted to take a small piece home for a
table centerpiece or other decoration, and who were always
obliged. Also exhibited are the Red Sea dugongs which Dr.
Gohar believes are a species unlike that found in any other part
of the world; the largest sea turtle ever found in the Red Sea;
mounted shore birds that cause visiting ornithologists to gape

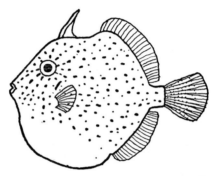

A NEW SPECIES OF FILEFISH FROM THE RED SEA

in awe; numerous invertebrates, sea plants, and even a collection of the local desert reptiles and mammals.

Speaking merely from an ichthyological viewpoint, looking
through this museum was like discovering hidden treasure. In
the first few days of examining the plectognath collection, I
found two amazing new species of the rare genera *Brachaluteres*
and *Paraluteres* that have baffled specialists trying to trace the
relationships between filefish and pufferfish. For here were filefish that blow up using the same mechanism as in pufferfish.
These genera had never before been known to occur in the

Red Sea or even in the Western Indian Ocean and these specimens extended their range remarkably.

A gigantic sting ray, like a big brown pancake with a whip from one end, hung on the museum wall waiting to be described to science for the first time. There were over sixty huge mounted skins of sixteen different species of sharks, ten rays, and three skates (including the formidable looking sawfish) and several hundred smaller skins (many colored) of the various reef fishes. The talented artist and taxidermist, Moawad Mohsen, had also made numerous paintings from life which recorded the colors, behavior, and other characteristics of rare, often unidentified, specimens collected at the Station.

There was such a wealth of material for me to go over! Dr. Gohar, pleased to have an ichthyologist study his fish collection for the first time, generously gave me permission to do whatever I thought best with it. And so I made a complete inventory and arranged the specimens in family groups. Then Dr. Gohar and I replanned the whole fish exhibit, and with the help of Mr. Mohsen and his assistants, we labeled everything that could be identified with both English and Arabic legends. We made plans to publish, in a series of scientific articles, our joint findings and collections of Red Sea fishes.

Some evenings I could hardly get through my dinner fast enough to go to the library and compare my day's catch with the specimens described by Ruppell and Klunzinger—the last ichthyological collectors in the Red Sea who had published their findings over seventy years ago. Sometimes I would find I had just collected dozens of a species so rare that it had previously been known and described from only one specimen. Or I might find I had a fish that wasn't in the books at all, and I would realize excitedly that it might be a species as yet unknown to science. Sometimes, by reviewing a series of my specimens, I would find an unknown age, color, or sex variation of a particular species.

Tracking down the names of these colorful sea gems I collected was as exciting as a detective search. Often as the night grew late, only the thought of our early morning sailboat trip to another coral reef, where we might spend hours of strenuous diving, could force me to close the books in time for a decent night's sleep.

And then I would go home to my little cottage and write to Ilias about my work—especially about the wonderful experiences spearfishing, for I knew he was very fond of swimming but had never tried it this way. I told him about the fishes I saw underwater, the poisonous kinds I caught, the sharks that didn't catch me.

Mail reached me only a few times a month but when it did, I could always count on many pages from Ilias. He kept me informed on all the news from home, of the opening of my parents' new restaurant and his frequent visits there to see them—and how he enjoyed the change from the intern's food at hospitals. My mouth watered as I read his descriptions of the dishes my stepfather made for him. But I consoled myself with the fact that never could the *sashimi* of a Japanese restaurant be delivered to the diner with the ease and freshness with which it was available to me every day at the Red Sea.

My small family of four had expanded since the days of my childhood. When my stepfather became a part of it, he strengthened the Japanese background and revived what was getting to be a dead language among mama, grandma, uncle, and me. A few years before that, however, uncle—perhaps overwhelmed by the thought of a blonde among the olive-skinned brunettes of our family—had married a peaches-and-cream beauty of Hungarian-Roumanian descent. Aunt Mary, a fluent trilinguist, was a European spice to the family that we all enjoyed. And now the addition of Greek flavoring was being gradually taken for granted. I thought of home often with a fondness and appreciation that comes after one has been away for months, yet without the home "sick" feeling that develops from loneliness.

18

Looking into Egypt's Past:
King Tut and Me

My stay in Egypt was not spent completely at Ghardaqa. There were a few times when I went to Cairo to give some lectures and then shopped for souvenirs in the ivory shops of Khan Khalili as excitedly as a typical female on a big sale day at Macy's. Then there were opportunities for short excursions to Suez, the Sinai peninsula, Qena, Luxor—sometimes in connection with my fish studies, sometimes without ichthyology in mind at all. On one such trip I went to a seldom seen ghost quarry, actually not very far from Ghardaqa, a place deep in the mountains.

A traveler on the Red Sea coast for the first time is usually surprised by the mountains there. For some reason most of us don't associate mountains with desert and yet mountains are one of the most characteristic features of the Red Sea coast. There are chains and chains of them, stretching over a thousand miles from Suez into the Sudan—fantastic, jagged peaks making an outline like the electrocardiogram of an excited person.

The first time I saw them was on the way to Ghardaqa from Suez. It was on a drive along rough and winding roads that went over hot stretches of flat desert, over cool coastal trails obliterated at some high tides, and through valleys between the mountains themselves which always loomed nearby. Dr. Gohar tore along these roads with veteran skill while Abdullah, the "chauffeur," slept in the back of the station wagon on my pile of luggage.

The mountain peaks were silhouetted against blazing rosy sunset and the calm surface of the sea reflected a solid red. "Perhaps this is why they called it the Red Sea," Dr. Gohar conjectured, although most biologists assume the Sea's name originates from the presence of a tiny red pigmented microorganism of the plankton life which, at certain seasons under the right conditions, proliferates extraordinarily and causes what we sometimes call "red tide."

But at this moment, my attention for once was more on the mountains than the sea. The strange mixtures of sedimentary and igneous barren rocky chains, which attracted the eye with their multivariations of yellows, browns, oranges, purples, and black, were now fading to a uniform gray. The jagged peaks seemed even more fantastic—like an illustration from a book of fairy tales. I half expected to see a giant peer from behind one. What was in those vast mountain ranges? Did anyone live in there? How could you get into them? Dr. Gohar answered my queries.

Except for a few desert patrol guard stations along the few remaining usable roads, hardly anyone lives in these mountains. Some bedouins, wandering Arabs, weave their way through on camelback sometimes taking months to cross through the ranges. They know where to find the few and far-between oases. The only other mammals you are apt to come across are gazelles, ibexes, and rats—and these on rare occasions. In one of these ranges there is a Coptic monastery, St. Paul's, supposed to be the oldest in the world. "Women visitors aren't allowed," Dr. Gohar dashed my hopes. Recently a group of scientists from the U.S. Navy Medical Research Unit, concerned with the problem of malarial control, went on an expedition into these mountains led by a bedouin. In a puddle, fed by a trickling stream in an oasis, they discovered a species of mosquito unknown to science. To make a trip into the mountains requires a good guide and at least two desert-equipped cars.

At one time, however, the mountains were not so desolate. In the first few centuries A.D., many thousands of people lived in them, in small square cities connected by a network of roads most of which lead to Qena on the Nile. In the time of Philadelphus, the second Ptolemy (285-247 B.C.), a port was built at Bernice and a road cut through the mountains from it to the Nile just south of Qena. A few hundred years later the Romans came to exploit the wealth in these mountains. They mined gold and quarried granite and built many good roads, with a sentry station almost every thirty miles. In these mountains they found the only source of "imperial porphyry"—a handsome red-purple rock, flecked with white or pink felspar crystals. This rare granite, inaccessible today, was brought to Rome and later to Constantinople where eight beautiful monolith columns can still be seen supporting the corner alcoves of St. Sophia.

Some weeks after I arrived at Ghardaqa, I had the chance to visit one of the most interesting remains of these Roman Stations at Mons Claudianus with a party of people from the Shell Oil Company. We left Ghardaqa at 6 A.M., got stuck in sand traps on the way, but before noon saw the rewarding sights of the ancient ruins. We wandered about in the square-walled enclosure of a once active Roman Station, the large temple beside it, and the quarry itself with remains of colossal columns that had broken and been abandoned there. One of these was sixty-five feet long and nine feet in diameter—one solid piece. It had been separated from the stone beds by the primitive but effective method of cutting wedge holes in the rock and then hammering pieces of wood into them. Then water was poured over the wooden wedges, so they swelled until they split off the gigantic piece of rock. When the columns were ready, thousands of Egyptian slaves and Roman outcasts pulled them across the hot desert mountains to the Nile.

The Red Sea and its reefs and fishes hardly seemed within a day's reach of so remote a place in the mountains. At the end of the hot and sticky ride out, the foothills grew smaller until they parted and we saw the Red Sea again in the distance, with the town of Ghardaqa sprinkled over the flat desert in between.

Ghardaqa or "Hurgada," its corrupted English name by which it is more commonly designated on maps in the English language, was once only a little fishing village. The word *ghardaqa* is the Arabic name of a small green desert bush that grows in some abundance there. It is thought that early fishermen on long trips along this barren coast made this their resting place, referring to it by the name of its green landmark. The springs in the nearby mountains probably supported the small community that started the fishing town of Ghardaqa.

The discovery of rich oil deposits in the sedimentary rocks along the Red Sea coast in recent times has led again to the exploitation of natural resources in areas barely touched since the days of the Romans. English companies started drilling oil fields. One of these is located at Ghardaqa, which grew from a simple fishing village to an industrial town where hundreds of natives were employed by the Shell Oil Company. In the last decade, however, the oil supply here has decreased sharply and the proportion of salt water to oil that the pumps bring up gets steadily larger. Today, Ghardaqa is changing to a ghost town. When the oil field gives out and operations cease, the water supply brought to the sizable community by English boats will also cease, and Ghardaqa may well shrink to just the little fishing village it was at first.

The history of the Red Sea coast has interesting mysteries. Where was Punt, the coastal city to which Queen Hatshepsut sent an expedition over 3,000 years ago? On a trip to Luxor, I looked at the original records of the expedition to Punt on the walls of the Temple of Queen Hatshepsut and I realized something which surprised me. The ancient Egyptians were ichthyologists too!

Piscine records on the tombs and temples are so accurate that the exact species of fish portrayed can be determined in most instances. A zoologist with no knowledge of Egyptology could differentiate, from a fragment of wall carving, the voyage to Punt from any voyage on the Nile—merely by the fishes depicted under the boat! I recognized a surgeon fish and a needle-fish that I had collected at the Red Sea just a few days before I came to look at these 3,000-year-old drawings.

But as the bed of the ancient Egyptian civilization was in the Nile Valley, it is natural that the fishes used most in their art work are of the Nile River. *Tilapia*, a mouth-breeding fish often kept in aquaria all over the world, was the most commonly depicted fish of the ancient Egyptians and is also the most important fish of Egypt today. A highly adaptable fish that tolerates brackish water, it has invaded all the estuaries and lakes connected to the Nile and has been artificially introduced and propagated in bodies of water not connected with the Nile. *Tilapia* is probably the most important single source of protein for the Egyptians of the past and present. It is found as a prominent figure in the jewelry of ancient Egyptians —strung together with sacred scarabs in necklaces and bracelets. In hieroglyphics it is the biconsonantal sign for *YN* as in the word *INYNT* meaning "valley." *Tilapia* is employed as a decoration in wall carvings of scenes along the Nile which also show over a dozen other types of fishes that can be recognized down to the exact

KING TUT

species, such as the "upside-down catfish" accurately drawn in the pose characteristic of its behavior.

Besides *Tilapia*, at least five other fishes and the fish scale itself are used in hieroglyphs to symbolize bi- and triconsonantal sounds. Thus I frequently saw the Nile pufferfish, mullet, barb, and the "elephant fish" or long-nosed mormyrid, scattered throughout the writings.

The ancient Egyptians were also spearfishermen. Once a magazine reporter in Cairo asked me to pose for a picture in a most exact position, spear held high at a precise angle, my head stiffly facing straight ahead, and my right foot behind my left foot in a rigid awkward stance. Why this unnatural pose? Because that's the way King Tutankhamen speared fish—according to a small golden statue found in his tomb! Pictures of King Tut and me were to be set together in the next issue of the magazine. The reporter must have considered me ungrateful that I declined the honor.

19

The Marine Station's Visitors

One morning our large shark nets brought up three "mermaids." Unfortunately all of them had died, but I was able to help with the job of making anatomical dissections and preparing the skeleton and skins. Dr. Gohar filled three quart bottles with their parasitic worms. As dugongs are herbivorous, feeding on eel grass on the sea bottom, I expected to find a long intestine, but even so was amazed when 120 feet of "rubber hose" came out of an eight-foot female. The actual skin and skeletal preparations were done by the Station's taxidermist.

Prince Ismail Hassan came for dinner that night. At a marine station he was expecting fresh fish of course. When he tasted the delicious steaks that seemed like a mixture of veal and pork, he commented politely, "I didn't know you could obtain such fine meat out here." "Oh yes," the gentle Dr. Gohar answered. "This is from a mermaid we caught today," and he continued eating like a serious cannibal.

In the week that followed, our versatile cook, Mohammed, prepared dugong meat in every way imaginable, fried, boiled, broiled, baked, and in spaghetti sauce. Three dugongs, over half a ton of tasty meat, can go a long way.

We were munching on the last of the mermaid meat at lunch one day, when the old *Rais,* the "chief" among the sailors, came rushing to tell us that a giant devilfish had been caught alive.

We ran out to see it. The prince came in his new golf togs and white umbrella, and I got my camera ready as the sailors hoisted the manta from the sea. When it fell free into the pool, it splashed around ferociously. Its giant "wings," with a spread of over ten feet, pounded down on the water surface, churning up the mud and gravel till the whole pool became opaque. After a while it calmed down and swam about like a graceful, giant black bat. It became the main attraction of all the fishes on display and was like a pet. It soon learned the limits of its relatively small enclosure and swam about in regular patterns, banking the turns like a great transoceanic air liner. It was magnificent to watch.

But as the days went by we sorrowfully realized the inevitable fate of this creature, which except for its monstrous size was harmless. Its huge mouth, big enough to accommodate the heads of three men, was merely a smooth concavity into which its owner sieved sea water in order to extract the tiny microorganisms on which it feeds. It would have been necessary to obtain plankton by the barrelsful to keep the manta from starving—this giant who would not touch a fish three inches long. It wasn't possible to obtain even a snack for him with our

limited plankton-collecting equipment. Some days later we had
the rare but rueful opportunity of making an anatomical dissection of our monstrous pet.

During my year at the Marine Station we had a number of
visitors; some stayed only a few days, others for weeks. There
was an Egyptian algologist, an English algologist, a party of
ornithologists, the Rector of Farouk University, the Vice-Rector
of Fouad University, two Egyptian princes, and the American
Ambassador—to mention only a few who were attracted to the
enchanting life among the coral ıeefs. King Farouk had a
palatial resthouse nearby but was said to use it infrequently,
though once when a group of us bumped into him unexpectedly
at a restaurant in Cairo, he pumped Dr. Gohar's hand and inquired about the Marine Station, expressing much interest in it.
Dr. Gohar always spoke well of his king and defended him as
a patron of marine biology, regardless of what others said about
him. "After His Majesty's first visit to the Station he sent us
presents of a glass-bottomed boat and many glass cabinets for
our museum so that the marine life, both living and preserved,
might be shown to more advantage to our visitors. He notifies
me to take charge when anything unusual happens in connection with marine life, as the time a deformed whale was washed
ashore at Suez and people claimed it to be a sea monster." And
indeed the ex-king deserves the credit for the single specimen
of one of the rarest plectognaths in the Red Sea—the cowfish.
Farouk himself had collected it and, recognizing it as an oddity,
had had it carefully preserved and sent to Dr. Gohar.

The most effortless way to catch a prized food fish I ever

witnessed was after a freak accident that occurred during a visit from the Rector of Farouk University, Mustafa Bey Amer, and his family. It was the first day of their short stay and Dr. Gohar was anxious to impress them with the wonders to be seen at his Marine Station and the Red Sea.

After breakfast, we were all sitting on the Director's back porch overlooking the sea and the little pier with its laboratories. We were discussing the fisheries problem. Egypt, flanked by two great seas, has to import nearly half the fish it consumes. Canned and smoked fish particularly are obtained from Norway, England, Turkey, Japan, and the United States. Of the local supply only twenty-five per cent comes from the seas; the main source is the Nile, its canals and particularly the brackish water lakes of the Nile delta.

The Red Sea is Egypt's smallest harvest grounds for its commercial fishes. Less than 5,000 tons were fished from this great sea in the last year. A survey made by a Greek fisheries research vessel in 1936 estimated that—if more fishermen in the Red Sea could be supplied with motor trawlers, refrigeration facilities, and modern equipment in general instead of mainly sailboats and primitive hand gear—at least 140,000 tons of fish, exclusive of sharks, could be taken *per month* from the Red Sea.

"Well, that figure may be a bit high," Dr. Gohar commented. "Most people fail to realize that the exceptionally jagged reefs and subterrane of the Red Sea would snag trawl nets more easily and present problems not found in Mediterranean waters. But there's no doubt about it—the Red Sea is underfished."

As if Dr. Gohar's words had been a cue, the calm sea surface suddenly began to churn. Hundreds then thousands of small fish leaped into the air as if the sea's purse had just exploded and released a store of silver coins. Then we saw what was the cause of the commotion. The backs and tails of over a hundred large jackfish cut the surface. Their powerful bodies slashed about as the jackfish tried to free themselves from the shallow water into which they had heedlessly chased their prey. A few of the jacks actually flapped out onto the beach. Mohammed and Shehat rushed to the water's edge and picked up a big jack by the tail with each hand. The fish then gave such powerful jerks in the air that it seemed they could wrench the men's arms out of the sockets. The Rector's two sons had leaped from their seats and run to the beach. We all watched the spectacle, pop-eyed.

Yes, Amer Bey and his family were impressed by the Red Sea.

During a lecture in Cairo at the American Embassy, I showed a color movie taken by the Professor of Biology of Fouad University some fourteen years before when he had visited the Marine Station. After the lecture, Jefferson Caffery, the American Ambassador, asked to see me in his office.

"Those marine animals in that film—they're amazing! Can a visitor to this Station really see those creatures alive?" I assured the Ambassador he could.

A few days after I returned to the Red Sea the newspapers announced that the Ambassador was coming to Ghardaqa by special plane for a two days' inspection of the Marine Station and the work I was doing there.

Gomah and I scrubbed up the lab. Dr. Gohar alerted the *Rais* to be prepared for a trip in the big sailboat in case the Ambassador and his party might accept an invitation to spend a day at sea. Mohammed needed no alerting. He could prepare a banquet for more people than the boat could hold, at the shortest notice.

The first day of his visit, the Ambassador toured the museum, labs, and outdoor pools—with sparkling eyes. Unlike some other diplomats who had visited the Station and seemed to think it behooved their dignity to maintain an aloofness to marine creatures, Ambassador Caffery was a pleasure to show around. He had dozens of questions to ask and seemed genuinely interested in the research studies going on. He showed an almost childish delight in holding the creatures we picked out of the aquaria and working, with his own fingers, the release mechanism in the dorsal fin of a triggerfish.

The ambassador was not a young man and he walked with a cane, but when Dr. Gohar invited him on a boat trip the next day, he not only came eagerly, but he brought his bathing suit and asked to go spearfishing with us. He admitted he wasn't a strong swimmer but he wanted to try a face mask and snorkel tube (a breathing device that enables you to inhale ample air while floating face down at the surface of the water and which closes automatically during dives). When we reached the reefs, it took only a few minutes for Mr. Caffery to learn the technique of underwater goggling. He was so excited seeing the reef life in its natural habitat, we could hardly lure him back to the boat for the hot meal awaiting us. When we did, he was bleeding from small coral cuts but bursting with exclamations about "the most wonderful experience I've ever had!"

20

The Most Important Visitor

Of all the visitors who came to the Red Sea, the most important for me was an M.D. from the States. In June, Ilias was able to take some weeks off from his work and come to see for himself this wondrous life of fishing which I had been writing him about so enthusiastically.

I went to the big city to meet him and we were married in a Greek Orthodox church near Khan Khalili bazaar in Cairo. It was a good excuse for a shopping spree which included two gold rings with our names carved inside in Arabic. Ilias' mother flew down from Athens for the occasion and acted as our *cubara* (best "man").

The ceremony was all in Greek and naturally I couldn't follow it; but I watched attentively as if I did. Things were going smoothly until the priest who was marrying us did what I thought was a strange thing. He stood in front of me with

Ilias' ring between the tips of his thumb and index finger, brought it to within an inch of my mouth, and nodded to me. I suppose any one in her right senses could have guessed what the priest wanted me to do. But it is strange how, at some of the most important moments in your life, your powers to think right can go amiss. For a second I got panicky for lack of knowing what to do. Then suddenly my mind flashed back to the days of my horned toad and communions at the altar of Mr. Stephans' little chapel. I didn't know what I was going to do with the ring, once I got it on my tongue, but anyhow I opened my mouth wide to receive it.

The priest looked aghast while Ilias quickly informed me, "You only have to kiss it."

The Bible was passed around next, but the priest wasn't taking any chances. When he lifted it to my lips, he stopped his Greek chanting and whispered to me in French, "Don't try to eat it, just kiss it."

During our honeymoon at the Red Sea, we studied fish together. Ilias became very much interested in sharks. He was surprised to learn how harmless many of the species are. We had a live collection of these in the pool outside the lab and Ilias now shows with pride a picture I took of him in this pool with seven nurse sharks swimming around, each longer than Ilias. You can actually swim up to a huge nurse shark and give it a kick, and it will only swim away from you. This is the type you usually see in the movies when a "courageous" man dives underwater, grabs hold of a shark, and stabs the poor harmless creature in the belly. But there are other types of sharks around the Red Sea which are not quite so sluggish and dull-toothed as the nurse shark.

The most savage looking shark in the Red Sea is undoubtedly the "Mako." We were glad to know it only from specimens in the Station's museum. A ten-foot female had been captured alive some time before. Before she died she gave birth to six babies. Ilias and I agreed that, pickled in formalin, these chubby little fellows—with their characteristically sharply pointed noses, large eyes, rudimentary second dorsal and anal fins, and symmetrically crescent unsharklike tail—looked cute. But their mama! Her monstrous set of teeth, each like an elongated curved spearhead, dwarfed those on the mounted twelve-foot tiger shark. Because of its spectacular habit of leaping out of the water, particularly when hooked, the Mako is a popular game fish. Its streamlined body and the fact that it is known to feed occasionally on the swift swordfish are evidences that this is one of the fastest swimming sharks known.

In Fars el Bahr, the largest fish market in Suez, I once saw the head of a big Mako on the counter. When I inquired about the rest of the body, I learned that it had been "sold out." It was somewhat surprising to find that sharks were eaten at Suez, for at Ghardaqa they are never eaten, and even Dr. Gohar with his gastronomical curiosity had never tried one.

My first experience eating shark had been in Kayangel, a far off little island in Micronesia. My native host served it raw. The odor from the decomposition products of urea that is stored in the flesh of sharks bothered me somewhat, but I have never forgotten my surprise at the tender and pleasant-tasting white meat that I finished with no effort. I had made a mental note to try shark properly cooked some day. What better opportunity than at Ghardaqa?

Mohammed's talents were again called on and he prepared one of the tastiest dishes I have ever had—steamed shark and onions with tomato sauce. The shark was as delicious as the tenderest breast of chicken and had the advantage of having no bones to bother either cook or gourmet. Mohammed had washed it well before cooking and although it had been alive that same morning, no offensive odor remained. Thus we had a new addition to our somewhat limited menu at Ghardaqa.

Aside from the Mako, there are at least two other types of sharks in the Red Sea that it is best to stay clear of when swimming: the tiger shark and the hammerhead. "Small" tiger sharks (up to five or six feet) can usually be identified by their stripes. The adults (which reach thirty feet, one of the largest species in the Red Sea aside from the harmless whale shark) lose these stripes. But it is said by the best authorities that there is no danger of confusing the "tiger" with any other shark because they have such a characteristic tooth shape (said to be handy for cutting through turtle shells) and the upper labial furrow or "lip" groove is exceptionally long. These are not exactly handy characteristics for underwater fishermen. However, if you should ever find yourself sliding into the buccal cavity of a tiger shark, you can't miss these features and you can at least have the satisfaction of knowing which species is swallowing you.

Tiger sharks seem to be more common in deep water although there are many records of them coming into shallow coastal waters and in some parts of the world they are a menace to bathers. The large specimen in the Station's museum was caught in only a few fathoms but was considered uncommon there. When spearfishing, Atiyah has no fear of any shark in shallow water. The cry of "*Gersh!*" will send him, spear in hand, in the direction you indicate, before he asks what kind or size it is. And a tiger shark, even with its poor eyesight, I'm sure could see Atiyah before Atiyah could tell it from a nurse shark. Perhaps the old spearfisherman has more faith than most of us in the ichthyological statement of fact that the tiger shark is generally rather sluggish—except when stimulated!

The hammerhead shark, with its small eyes located on the ends of peculiar lateral extensions on its head, is an easy fish to identify. Even Atiyah may well be able to diagnose a hammerhead underwater before it can spot him. Native fishermen at Ghardaqa all agree that this shark is highly dangerous and the numerous large skins in the Station's museum attest to the belief that it is a fairly common shark in the Red Sea. Although hammerheads do not grow much larger than thirteen feet, they are known all over the world as "man-eaters" and have attacked people in shallow water with apparently no provocation. The old *Rais* will tell you with dramatic gesticulations about the time a hammerhead attacked him while he was standing in only a few feet of water adjusting a reef marker on the coral next to the Station. It was a rare incident that took place

a long time ago, but the deep scars on the calves of the *Rais*
support his story about the ferocity of the attack.

Aside from the Mako, Tiger, and Hammerhead, there are
over a dozen other kinds of sharks found in the region of
Ghardaqa. These are the more common species and fortunately
most of them are harmless. Ilias and I studied all of them and
I was glad to find it did not stop him from spearfishing as he
weighed the evidence reasonably and realized that our chances
of meeting a dangerous species underwater were poor.

In Cairo we had bought a speargun and an extra snorkel
tube and face mask for Ilias. I had not invested in a speargun
before because I found, when testing it in the store for the first
time, that it took all my strength to adjust the rubber sling into
shooting position and while I did, the gun handle pressed pain-
fully in my stomach. Ilias of course could pull the sling into
place on the spear-shaft with ease the first time he tried it. After
we had the gun a while I found the easy way to load it by holding the gun against my hip bone. I also discovered that underwater, especially after the rubber sling was used a number of
times, it was really quite simple and fast to load. However,
until Ilias came and even during most of his visit, I used simple
spears with long wooden handles of various sizes which Dr.
Gohar had thoughtfully ordered for the Station when I told
him about the inconveniences of the all-metal spears that the
natives used. Besides, a simple spear was more convenient for
catching some of the fish I was after—large sting rays, for
example, often tangled the line attached to the speargun and
their dangerous tails could get uncomfortably close to the diver

catching them with a speargun. But for most fishes the speargun or arbalete is more efficient and easier to aim with.

After his first dive underwater into a coral garden, when the shaft from his speargun sank into a parrotfish, Ilias was sold on this sport. He became the most ardent spearfisherman I have ever seen. At last, I had found someone who was still raring to go when I was ready to quit.

It was not until after two weeks of spearfishing at the Red Sea together that Ilias and I had our first uncomfortable underwater experience. We were on the outer edge of a crescent-shaped reef not far from the Station, where we went almost every day for an hour or two of spearfishing just before lunch. Ilias was playing with a speckled sea bass, trying to spear it during the brief moments when it peered out of one of several holes in the coral. Gradually he was learning the pattern of the connecting branches to all the holes. He never brought his face or hands too close to these holes. (Only a few days before, when he did look closely into a reef crevice, the head of a moray eel, with its open mouth and jagged teeth, looked back at him.) Finally he aimed his speargun and shot into a hole, but he then had to reload it in disgust as the bass' big eyes watched him from another. I watched the game in amusement but then spotted a rare butterfly fish and chased after it around to the other side of a large group of corals.

The butterfly fish scurried down the steeply sloping reef and hid among some branched corals. I dived for it with my spear ready, but my aim was bad. I dived again and again trying to locate its hiding spot. And then, for some unknown reason,

I suddenly glanced behind me. Less than four yards away was an enormous fish. My first impression from its size was that it was a shark. But as I got a better look at its large silver form, lying motionless near the surface of the water, it was plain to see that this fish was a barracuda of gigantic proportions. It had turned its profile and its whole length was visible. Its sharp eye was unmistakably watching me. How long it had been there I don't know. I must have been safe, however, for if a barracuda intends to strike, I doubt that he thinks it over very long. I took no chances and started to back away slowly to a shallow part of the reef. I decided it was best in a situation like this not to swim away quickly and create an image of flying arms and legs, but to let the barracuda continue to see my body as a whole. After all, I was about his equal in length.

Then I remembered my last look at innocent Ilias on the other side of the group of corals—blissfully diving down among the reef holes trying to locate his fish, a deeply tanned body in dark blue bathing trunks, with feet waving about in sparkling new white sneakers looking, from a distance, like two little fishes—nice barracuda bait!

I scanned the water quickly and when I saw a snorkel tube break the surface, I called out hoping my husband would hear me. He lifted his head and I shot a glance at where I could still see the large shadowy form out in the clear water, separated from Ilias by only a cluster of corals. Then I shouted firmly, trying not to alarm him too much. "Ilias, come onto the reef immediately." He detected a very serious tone in my voice and answered, "Stay there. I'll get the boat." Before I could stop him, he swam out into the open water toward our rowboat. His arms churned bubbles in the water and his white sneakers, going full speed, trailed behind as he headed into the barracuda's path.

But he made it! A quick lift of his arms and he was safely in the boat. He rowed over to where I was standing on the reef in just a few feet of water.

"It was a shark, wasn't it?" he guessed. When I told him it was no dull-eyed shark but a large barracuda, he was not too impressed. For several days, however, I could not enjoy goggling underwater. I had to look behind me every few seconds and I always carried a vivid picture of that barracuda. But in all the months that followed, I never met another even half that size.

Some days later, when the effects of the barracuda incident had worn off, we were spending a day spearfishing and collecting at Sharks' Bay, the beauties of which Ilias was seeing for the first time. He had yet to see a shark face-to-face and was becoming almost impatient. "I thought you said we'd see sharks out here for sure," he commented after we had been in the water about half an hour. But we were having excellent spearfishing and had caught squirrel fish, surgeon fish, a sting ray, a scorpion fish, and a huge porcupine fish. We had gotten a good distance apart when some time later a shark about four and one-half feet long came suddenly from behind a wall of coral and swam past me.

It was a specimen of *Triaenodon obesus* (meaning the three-cuspid-toothed fat one) named by Ruppell who first described

it from the Red Sea in 1835. This species may be classed in the
family of sharks popularly referred to as "true sharks" (*Carcha-
rhinidae*)—the only group of fishes with a nictitating membrane
in the eye and bladelike teeth, enabling them to wink at you
and take off your foot in the same moment. This particular
species, however—blunt-nosed, small-toothed, and among the
less streamlined of the carcharhinids—seldom exceeds six feet
and is generally considered harmless. It is easily recognized
from a distance by the white tips on its dorsal and caudal fins.

"There's a white-tipped shark coming your way," I called
out to my husband. That should satisfy him, I thought. With
underwater magnification it will seem a good six feet in size.
He peered around in anticipation but at the same time backed
toward the shallow part of the reef. "I see it," Ilias yelled back
and then he added, "There's two of them!" He started swimming faster and then as I watched he stopped, looked underwater through his face mask, and disappeared from the surface.

I caught my breath and wondered how big the second shark
was and if it were the same harmless species. Suppose it were
a hammerhead or tiger shark! I estimated the seconds. If Ilias
had dived of his own accord, he should be up for air now. His
head finally broke the surface and he stood up on the shallow
reef. "Look, I speared a fish," he said triumphantly as he waved
his spear with a parrot fish on the end.

But don't conclude that we had become fearless of sharks.
Only a few days later a large fellow about eight feet long appeared suddenly from beneath us, and in all due respect, we
leaped into our handy canoe so fast we almost overturned it.

The shark was a more streamlined species and the dark edges of its fins suggested it was one of the less harmful species, but we were satisfied to forgo further identification.

On our last spearfishing trip together, Ilias made a record catch. In less than three hours he had thirty good-sized specimens, including a rare butterfly fish I had never obtained before. He even caught two fish with one shot from his speargun that day. It was a grand finale for him. Then he had to leave for the States where he had an appointment in the Orthopedics Division of the Buffalo General Hospital.

In the next few months, I had to spend more hours working in the lab, packing fish and writing up my notes, than I could on the reefs. Time seemed to move at two extremes—too fast for me to finish all I wanted to do at the Red Sea—too slowly for me to be separated from Ilias.

When I finished my work in Egypt, I joined Ilias in Buffalo. From the warm tropic water of the Red Sea, I came to a city covered with snow. The dark tan, that conveniently passed me off as an Egyptian woman during my last days in Cairo when riots were starting in the streets, soon faded as I again took up the life of an apartment dweller. The job still remains of assimilating the hundreds of pages of notes that I've brought back. It's not the most exciting part in the life of an ichthyologist, but it is one of the most important. There is little point to traveling around the world and learning new things about fishes in far-off places, if you don't make your findings available for the possible use of others.

By publishing my scientific results in a series of papers in the journal of Egypt's Marine Biological Station, I will have the good fortune to be able to use a number of color plates among the illustrations—something almost unheard of in scientific journals in this country. For me it's a special incentive. In scientific writing there are so many cold facts to be reported that there is no

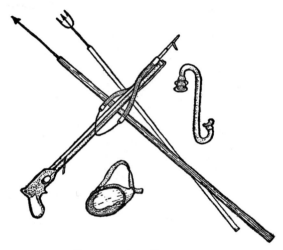

SPEARFISHING EQUIPMENT

place for the type of description that marine biologists, who work with animals and in an environment of such beauty as I have, would like to include. I, at least, find it hard to restrain the desire to embellish my reports with personal impressions. To be allowed even one color plate in these rather stiff formal articles consisting largely of long scientific names, tables of measurements, fin counts, descriptions of viscera, etc., gives me a feeling of aesthetic release that perhaps the conservative businessman feels when he tops off a dull gray suit and plain white shirt with a red tie.

Sometimes when I'm studying my notes, I come across a notation on a special fish that Ilias speared and then I interrupt him from one of his medical books and say, "Remember the time you speared this fish at Fenidir reef?" Suddenly we are back again in the Red Sea and corals are all around us; a speckled sea bass is tempting Ilias from a crevice in the corals; schools of whiskered goatfish and green and pink parrot fish parade by us; and familiar clown fish dance among the tentacles of sea anemones as shimmering rays of sunlight set all the colors of the reef aglow—even though it be a dark night and snow is falling past the windows of our apartment.